A COMPLETE GUIDE TO
BRITISH DRAGONFLIES

A COMPLETE GUIDE TO BRITISH DRAGONFLIES

Andrew McGeeney

JONATHAN CAPE
THIRTY-TWO BEDFORD SQUARE LONDON

First published 1986
Copyright © 1986 by Andrew McGeeney

Jonathan Cape Ltd, 32 Bedford Square, London WC1B 3EL

British Library Cataloguing in Publication Data

McGeeney, Andrew
A complete guide to British dragonflies.
1. Dragon-flies – Great Britain
I. Title
595.7'33'0941   QL520.24.G7

ISBN 0-224-02307-1

Title page illustration: Male Club-Tailed Dragonfly
(*Gomphus vulgatissimus*)

Photoset by Rowland Phototypesetting Ltd,
Bury St Edmunds, Suffolk
Printed in Spain by Graficas Estella, S.A.

To Kathleen and Patrick –
for all their encouragement

Male Emerald Damselfly (*Lestes sponsa*)

Male Southern Blue Damselfly (*Coenagrion mercuriale*) – note the extensive sky-blue colouring

CONTENTS

Acknowledgments   ix

Introduction   1

    Structure   2
    Reproductive Behaviour   3
    Life Cycle   5
    Habitat   10
    Conservation   12
    Observation and Study   13
    Collecting Larvae   14

British Dragonflies   15

Glossary   103
Key to the Identification of Adults   107
Key to the Identification of Larvae   118
Further Reading   128
Check List   129

Index   132

Male Beautiful Demoiselle (*Calopteryx virgo*)

ACKNOWLEDGMENTS

I am pleased to thank the many friends and acquaintances who have helped in the production of this book. Most of all I would like to express my gratitude to my partner Mandy Kuijvenhoven. The project has been a joint effort between us, we have shared the challenges and worked together at every stage.

I am very grateful to Dr Reinhold Turk who not only found and photographed the parasitic mites but offered encouragement and constructive criticism at various stages of the book's progress. I wish to thank the Zoology Department of the National Museum of Wales, Cardiff, for permission to reproduce the scanning electron micrograph photographs on page 9. I am also very grateful to Bob Kemp for the photographs of female *Somatochlora arctica*.

I have gained a great deal from the many people with whom I have shared field trips in the past couple of years; Betty Smith and Eddie Ryan have been particularly helpful. I am indebted to others for their assistance in locating useful sites and providing information on some of our rarer species. In particular I wish to express my thanks to M. Jean-Paul Dommanget, Prof. B. Kiauta, Prof. E. Schmidt and Dr Marcel Wasscher. I am most grateful to the Royal Entomological Society for the use of their library facilities.

All at Jonathan Cape who have shared in the book's creation have been energetic and professional in their various ways.

Female Club-Tailed Dragonfly (*Gomphus vulgatissimus*) emerging from its larval skin.
Photographed by the river Thames in June.

INTRODUCTION

Dragonflies are among the largest, most colourful and fastest flying of insects. There are more than 5,000 species in the world, including the giants in the jungles of South America with a 13 cm. body and a wingspan of 18 cm. During Carboniferous times, when present-day coal was a living fern tree, the largest dragonfly of all time, *Meganeura monyi*, used to glide on a 75 cm. wingspan.

Representatives of all the European families of dragonflies make up the thirty-nine breeding species and two regular migrants found in the British Isles (including the whole of Ireland), and these are the subject of this book. To these forty-one we can add another seven accidental or irregular visitors and three residents of the Channel Isles. See the check list on pages 129–31 for further details. Since the 1950s three British species have become extinct and something like a third of the existing species are in danger, although all may still be found on the Continent. On the positive side, a new species for Ireland was first recorded in 1981, and there may be others waiting to be discovered.

In the Far East the larvae are eaten as a delicacy, much as we might eat shrimps, and in Colombia coloured dragonfly wings provide an attractive nose ornament. For the Japanese the dragonfly is an important cultural symbol. Over thirty species have popular names, and in art and literature they represent playfulness and victory in war. Another name for Japan is Akitsushima, which means Dragonfly Island.

In Europe dragonflies receive less attention. Sometimes they reach the headlines when vast numbers migrate, as in 1972, and the spectacular passage of an estimated 2,000 million in 1862 darkened the skies of East Prussia from dawn until dusk. The Four-Spotted Chaser *Libellula quadrimaculata* has a ten-year cycle of migrations. The actual stimulus to swarm and move off results from the cumulative effect of population pressure, parasitic irritation and specific climatic conditions.

Dragonflies have a primitive flight mechanism compared with other advanced flying insects, such as bees. Each wing works independently and cannot reach more than thirty beats per second. Bees fly by contracting the whole thorax to provide co-ordinated beats of three hundred per second. Despite their primitive structure, dragonflies can reach speeds of over thirty kilometres per hour, they can hover, loop the loop and fly in reverse with ease. In fact, they live by catching the more sophisticated fliers.

The scientific name given to dragonflies is Odonata. This order consists of two sub-orders: true dragonflies, the Anisoptera, and damselflies, the Zygoptera. Damselflies are generally smaller insects with narrow delicate bodies and four similar-shaped wings with different venation from true dragonflies. They flutter among marginal vegetation or fly close to the water surface; when they settle, the wings are usually folded together over the back. The eyes are positioned on each side of the head, giving the appearance of a double-ended rattle. True dragonflies have thicker bodies and compound eyes that meet, or almost meet. The more robust true dragonflies can be further divided into Hawkers and Darters. Usually Hawkers have long, almost cylindrical abdomens and are so called from their habit of tirelessly patrolling a patch of countryside in search of food or mates. They are powerful fliers and may remain at a tantalizing height, many metres from the ground. Darters are shorter, with abdomens that are sometimes broader, and have the habit of choosing a favourite perch, such as a pale reed or twig, on which to sun themselves. The perch is used as a base from which rapid sorties are made in order to catch food or see off rival males.

Dragonfly larvae do not receive the same attention as the winged adult, probably because most of them are a dull brown or olive green and live a secretive existence among pondweed and silt. In fact, they are fascinating. As we shall see later, the larvae are ferocious carnivores, with a unique method of jet propulsion and respiration, using a hydraulically powered lower jaw to catch prey. But confident identification of a dragonfly larva requires the use of a good hand-lens or microscope. There is an identification key on pages 118–27, but even using this, it will not always be possible to determine the species with certainty.

Structure

The technical terms which are used to describe the structure of a dragonfly may be found in the glossary on pages 103–6.

Looking at the structure in detail, it can be seen that it is divided into three major segments, the head, the thorax and the abdomen, with a small prothorax linking the first two.

The head is large for an insect, due primarily to the two bulbous compound eyes, each of which has 30,000 facets. The large eyes are very sensitive to movement up to ten metres away and their structure provides all-round vision. In addition, three single-faceted eyes, called ocelli, are positioned on top of the head. Below the frons and clypeus, which form a broad nose, are the massive upper and lower jaws that give the order its name (Odonata means toothed). The serrated mouthparts are ideally suited to the dragonfly's carnivorous feeding habits. The antennae are poorly developed organs of smell and touch placed on top of the head between the eyes. The head is able to swivel in almost any direction, partly because of the prothorax which joins it to the thorax. The prothorax of each species is a distinctly sculpted disc, ensuring that only a male of the same species can grip the female's prothorax with his anal appendages or claspers during pairing. This species' difference is also of some help in identifying a dragonfly in the hand.

The thorax consists of two fused segments containing the large wing muscles and the beginning of the gut. The wings have become tilted backwards during the process of evolution and the legs have become correspondingly pushed forward. A dragonfly's six long and bristly legs are almost useless for walking, but are sufficient for the insect to grip on to a perch when it lands. In flight, the legs and their tibial spines form a basket for scooping up prey which is then passed forwards by the feet, or tarsi, for consumption by the mandibles.

Female Banded Demoiselle (*Calopteryx splendens*) eating a mayfly

The four wings consist of a double layer of membrane kept rigid by a fine network of veins. The leading edge has a triple row of thicker veins forming the costa, and a node or cross-member roughly halfway along these veins, all of which increases the rigidity of the wings. Almost at the tip of each wing is a dark rectangular patch, known as the pterostigma. The pattern of veins is an important means of identifying and classifying dragonflies, in particular two triangular areas near the base of the wing in Anisoptera and a rectangular configuration similarly placed in Zygoptera.

The long abdomen consists of ten segments, with the vestige of an eleventh, and at its tip are the anal appendages used for pairing. Male true dragonflies have two upper and one lower anal appendages, while male damselflies have two upper and two lower ones. Females lack the lower appendages, but have an ovipositor or a vulvar scale under the eighth or ninth segment. The male genital opening is on the ninth segment, but as a consequence of the dragonfly's unique method of pairing, sperms are transferred to organs on the ventral surface of the second and third segments. Some species even have small protuberances called auricles to help guide the female's genitalia to the male's secondary genitalia. Most of the interior of the abdomen is taken up with the alimentary canal.

In common with other insects, dragonflies breathe by means of tracheae, one pair to each segment. Instead of lungs and a blood system to carry oxygen round the body, the tracheae form a network of tubes of progressively finer diameter to transport oxygen directly to the interior of the body. This is one functional limitation on the size of dragonflies and is the reason why species the size of vultures are not seen swooping over our lakes and rivers.

Insects are cold-blooded, which means that they need to employ a variety of techniques in order to maintain an optimum working temperature. Perching dragonflies will settle near the ground to warm up and move higher or shield their body with their wings as the ambient temperature rises. Large Hawkers keep cool by gliding every so often, and by altering the circulation between the thorax and abdomen. Some species change colour from a dull purplish grey to bright blue as a way of absorbing or reflecting heat.

There are records of Darter dragonflies surviving a night frost of −8°C and waiting for the sun to thaw off the frozen dew. In fact, some dragonflies roost on the east side of trees to catch the first warmth of sunrise. A certain amount of grooming and wing whirring is required before lift-off on a cool day.

Reproductive Behaviour

Although adult dragonflies may range far and wide across a variety of different habitats, in order to breed they must lay their eggs near or in water, so that the larvae may develop in a suitable aquatic environment. Typically, the first stage is for the mature male to visit potential breeding sites regularly (these are referred to as the encounter or rendezvous sites). At almost any unpolluted weedy pond in late summer, the number of visiting male Common Darters, *Sympetrum striolatum*, gradually increases to a peak around midday. Each individual selects a few prominent landing sites or perches from which to make frequent food forays or attacks on rival males. Many other species of dragonfly are also territorial; the larger the dragonfly the larger the defended area. Clashes are frequent as newcomers try to force their way into the airspace above the pond. A defender will try to fly under the attacker, so as to push it away from the water surface. This may lead to combatants cartwheeling down into the water. Some species swarm over a communal territory, others timeshare the encounter site.

Once the males have spent a week or so defending their territories and survived in the suitable habitat, the females will have matured sexually and begun to make visits from the surrounding countryside. Usually, the females are less conspicuous in their colouring; for example, among the Libellulidae in the British Isles the males are mostly sky blue or vermilion red, while their female counterparts are various shades of brown and yellow.

In Britain, a distinctive courtship display has been recorded for three species; the two *Calopteryx* damselflies, where the males flutter their metallic-

A pair of Yellow-Winged Darters (*Sympetrum flaveolum*) mating in the wheel position

coloured wings, and *Platycnemis pennipes*, where the distinctive white legs are used as a sign stimulus. Physical incompatibility usually prevents pairing between different species.

The unique form of copulation performed by dragonflies may appear bizarre at first sight. It begins with the male transferring sperm from the genital opening on the ninth abdominal segment to the accessory genitalia on the second and third segments some time after arriving at the breeding site or immediately before copulation. This can be partly explained by the fact that the male has to use the appendages on the end of his abdomen to grasp the female, thus preventing sperms being transferred directly. The evolutionary origin of this method of pairing is still debated among odonatists. Almost as soon as a female arrives at the breeding site, she will be pursued by one or more of the mature males. A male will attempt to grasp the thorax of the female from above and place his claspers around the narrow 'neck' between her head and the prothorax, or the head itself. If they are both of the same species, the male appendages will fit the shape of the prothorax exactly. A receptive female will then grip the male appendages by pressing her head back so that the male can release his legs and fly with her in

tandem. Almost immediately the female will curl her abdomen forwards so that her genital opening is pressed against the sperm-carrying accessory genitalia of the male. As was mentioned earlier, some species even have protuberances, called auricles, on the male's second abdominal segment to guide the female into the correct position. The pair may remain in what is called the wheel position for a few seconds, for five to ten minutes, or longer – even over an hour. In the latter case, they will fly into nearby vegetation or up into trees to avoid disturbance from other males or predators.

Recent research has brought to light the intriguing fact that in some species the male is equipped with a bristly penis. In the dragonflies that have been investigated, the initial stage of copulation involves the removal of rival sperms inside the female; only then will the male deposit his own sperms to fertilize the eggs.

Once copulation is completed, the female must seek suitable sites to deposit her eggs. There are two kinds of eggs. Either they are endophytic eggs, to be laid by an ovipositor in vegetation or mud, in which case they are elongated and oval, or they are round exophytic eggs deposited freely in the water from the vulvar scale as the abdomen is dipped below the surface. In some cases the male has no further part to play and he will fly off. The male of some species, however, will stay to guard the female as she releases her eggs. In the Common Darter *Sympetrum striolatum*, the male flies in tandem with the female to prevent rival males

A pair of Common Darters (*Sympetrum striolatum*) egg-laying in tandem

from mating with her and at the same time gives added lift as she hovers above the water. The female Golden-Ringed Dragonfly *Cordulegaster boltonii*, one of our largest species, has a long and distinctive ovipositor with which she thrusts eggs into the soft mud that collects beside running water. Among the blue damselflies, such as the Azure Damselfly *Coenagrion puella*, the male remains above the water surface while the female oviposits eggs in the stems of underwater vegetation, sometimes remaining submerged for minutes at a time.

Life Cycle

The incomplete metamorphosis in dragonflies consists of three stages, namely the egg, the larva, and the adult or imago. In some senses, the sexually mature imago is the larva's means of ensuring dispersion and the continuation of the species, because many larvae live for two or more years, depending on conditions, while the winged adult may remain alive for a few weeks at the most.

Dragonfly eggs – greatly enlarged

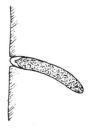

Emperor Dragonfly
Anax imperator

Ruddy Darter
Sympetrum sanguineum

Brilliant Emerald
Somatochlora metallica

Emerald Damselfly
Lestes sponsa

If the egg is fertile, it will change from cream to a reddy brown within twenty-four hours of being released. It may remain in a dormant state for a long time, as it does in some Aeshnidae and Lestidae, if this is the means by which the species survives the winter. Other species reach maturity and hatch within two to five weeks. The prolarva emerges by wriggling free of the egg. If it is an endophytic species, laid in vegetation, the egg may have a protuberance or cone preventing the plant from sealing the only exit for the first instar. The prolarva may wait only a matter of seconds, or at the most a few hours, before shedding its skin. The larva then develops and increases in size through a further ten to fifteen instars until the time comes for it to emerge from its aquatic habitat into the air. After the fourth moult, the wingcases develop and the eyes increase in size until, in the Anisoptera, they meet just prior to emergence.

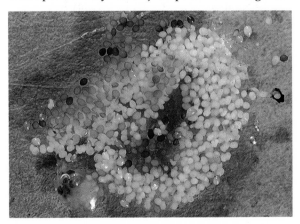

Eggs of the Common Darter (*Sympetrum striolatum*). The brown-yellow ones are fertile.

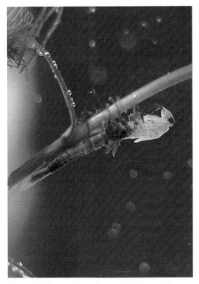

Damselfly larva changing its skin

Hawker dragonfly larva, Southern Hawker (*Aeshna cyanea*)

Darter dragonfly larva, Four-Spotted Chaser (*Libellula quadrimaculata*)

Anyone breeding larvae in captivity can collect the shed skin, or exuvia, and dry-mount it on white card. It will then be possible to have a record of the various stages of larval growth.

The larvae of Zygoptera differ from those of Anisoptera in many ways. First, they are slimmer and more delicate-looking, with a narrow abdomen terminating in three leaf-like gills or caudal lamellae. The caudal gills do not seem to be essential for breathing, for an individual may lose one or more when a predator takes a snap at it. However, they are useful as a means of propulsion when the damselfly larva wriggles through the water. In both sub-orders the larvae may move by slow creeping movements but the anisopteran larvae are also able to expel water rapidly from the rectum and so move by jet propulsion. A brachial basket inside the rectum ensures that Anisopteran larvae can breathe without external caudal gills. The dragonfly larvae are more squat and bulbous in the shape of their abdomen, but otherwise structurally similar to damselfly larvae.

Dragonfly larvae can see only a short distance, but they are very sensitive to movement of any kind. If the moving object is smaller than they are

Seventeen exuviae of the Common Blue Damselfly (*Enallagma cyathigerum*) on one stem

it is assumed to be potential prey and followed with interest. Should small fish, insect larvae or suchlike swim within striking distance of a hungry dragonfly larva, they will soon be caught by its modified lower jaw. This unique structure remains concealed below the larva's mouth and is

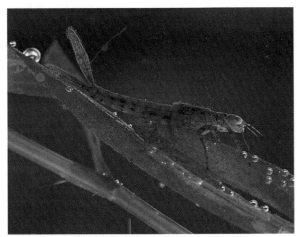

Damselfly larva, Red-Eyed Damselfly (*Erythromma najas*)

Southern Hawker (*Aeshna cyanea*) larva ready to emerge (note the swollen wingcases)

sometimes referred to as the mask. It is spatulate in shape with a pair of movable palps furnished with sharp hooks and bristles. Its effectiveness as a means of catching prey is enhanced by the hydraulic arm which rapidly thrusts it forwards. Dragonfly larvae are voracious eaters and will rapidly consume other living creatures in an aquarium, including their own kind. When rearing larvae it is best to keep the food supply well stocked and to ensure that the larger species are kept in separate containers. They themselves become prey to larger carnivores in the wild, such as fish and ducks, but the abdominal spines on anisopteran larvae prevent their being swallowed from behind. Some species remain concealed in the muddy bottom, waiting for food to swim near. They usually rely on touch rather than sight and have a bristly body which traps silt and further increases their concealment. Other species hunt among the weeds or plant stems of emergent vegetation. Some young larvae of Aeshnids have a banded coloration which acts as an inhibitor to older conspecifics, which might be tempted to feed on them. In general, dragonfly larvae rely on camouflage colouring and remaining still to induce their food to come to them.

Some species develop in less than a year; others, such as the Brown Hawker *Aeshna grandis*, remain at the larval stage for two years. This is partly determined by food supply, but the most impor-

tant factor is the time and form of adult emergence. Species that emerge during the spring do so in a highly synchronized manner, often with an early peak of just a few days. The Emperor Dragonfly *Anax imperator* and the Large Red Damselfly *Pyrrhosoma nymphula*, for example, emerge within a short space of time determined by day-length and temperature. They also have a diapause or resting stage in the final instar, to ensure that late developers catch up and can emerge on time. Summer species, such as the Common Darter *Sympetrum striolatum* and the Emerald Damselfly *Lestes sponsa*, do not have a synchronized emergence and may metamorphose throughout the season. Very often they will overwinter in the egg stage and grow rapidly as larvae in the warmer springtime.

Emergence is probably the most vulnerable time for a dragonfly. Having left the relative safety of a camouflaged larval state underwater, it must remain exposed and unable to fly until its wings have dried. A day or so before the final metamorphosis, the larva will move to shallower, warmer water and find a suitable object, such as the river bank, or an upright stem that extends into the air above. It may even take a look above the water surface, but slip back again to wait until the time is right. Most species emerge under the protection of darkness; the larva climbs up the stem or bank of earth and dries off its skin in the early morning air. Eventually, a split appears along the back of the thorax. The head, legs, wings and thorax are pulled free and the insect rests with its head held back until its legs harden. It is then safe for the dragonfly to hold on to the larval skin and finally free its abdomen. The wings unfold from their crumpled state and the body extends to its full length before hardening. Newly emerged dragonflies have a pale coloration that takes some time to develop, and the wings have a shiny quality until the fluid dries out between the veins. The main predators at this stage in its life are hunting spiders and birds. Should a dragonfly survive so far, its first instinct on drying out is to fly away from water. For some damselflies this may mean moving a few metres into the surrounding vegetation, but the larger species of dragonfly may travel many kilometres after leaving the emergent site in an almost vertical take-off.

Dragonflies take varying lengths of time to mature. The Emperor Dragonfly *Anax imperator* may take two weeks to become sexually mature and gain its full coloration, during which time it will avoid any stretch of water it comes across. The intensity of colouring is a useful indicator of a dragonfly's age, particularly with males, which very often have the same pigmentation as females before acquiring the distinctive markings of their own sex. Wing colour is another indicator of age in some species, although there is no hard and fast rule. Some species develop wing colours early on, while others gradually acquire tints with age.

Most damselflies have an average life of one or two weeks, with a maximum of eight weeks. True dragonflies live on average for two to three weeks, six at the most.

The brilliant colours worn by many dragonflies make them attractive creatures in the countryside, but a subsequent visit to a museum can be a disappointment when one is confronted with a drawerful of dried brown insects. The eyes in particular rapidly lose their reflective jewel-like quality soon after death. The reason why some species fade and others remain almost as colourful is due, in the main, to different methods of pigmentation. Metallic, iridescent species such as the Emeralds have an external reflective form of pigmentation that survives death, as does the exter-

Blue-Tailed Damselfly (*Ischnura elegans*) trapped in a spider's web

nal powder-blue pruinescence found on some of the Libellulidae. Those species where the pigment is contained within or beneath the skin usually lose their brilliance unless special precautions are taken with their preservation.

Sheer speed and aerial agility ensure that the larger dragonflies avoid serious predation. Hobbies are known to catch dragonflies and so are swallows. The smaller and feeble-flying damselflies have many predators: birds, the anisopteran dragonflies, and the sundew plant. When a damselfly that has settled on a plant is approached, it may slip behind the stem for concealment. If any dragonfly is picked up by the body, it will curl its abdomen forwards, mimicking the actions of a stinging insect. While all dragonflies are completely harmless, this curling action may be sufficient to scare any captor into releasing the insect, particularly if it is accompanied by a nip from the serrated mouthparts. This could be the origin of the country name 'horse-stinger'. Another plausible explanation for such a misnomer is that an entomologist may have misheard the Dorsetshire dialect name of 'hosetinger', which roughly translated means long-bodied thing.

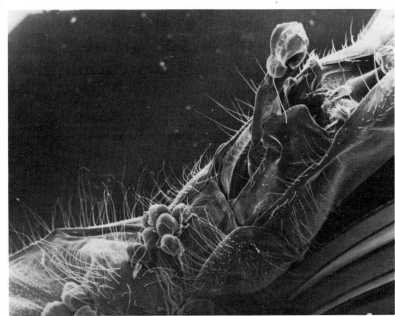

Above left, parasitic water mite larvae (Hydracnellae) clustered underneath the thorax and first abdominal segment of a male Variable Blue Damselfly *Coenagrion pulchellum*

Above right, water mite larvae are clustered on the thorax and first segment. The damselfly's penis can be seen protruding from the second abdominal segment in the top right-hand side of the picture

Right, in some species the water mite larva develops from an egg laid by the aquatic adult and in its final instar seeks out a damselfly as its host. It subsequently transfers itself from the larval skin to the winged adult insect during the damselfly's emergence. The damselfly host transports the mite larva during its own dispersal, and on returning to water to breed the mite larva drops off and changes into an adult water mite.

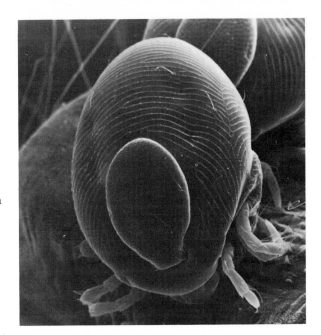

Habitat

Adult dragonflies may be found in a wide variety of habitats, some a fair distance from the essentially aquatic requirements of the larval stage. After all, the only necessity for visiting water is in order to pair and deposit eggs. Nevertheless, it may be important for males to attempt to remain at the breeding site for some time and to fight off competition so as to make sure they have the greatest chance of mating with a visiting female. In some species, the latter may visit the breeding site once, pair and oviposit in concealed vegetation, never to be seen near water again. On a woodland walk in summer it is possible to see a wide variety of species, from the high-flying Migrant Hawker *Aeshna mixta* and Brown Hawker *A. grandis* patrolling back and forth along the rides and clearings, to red *Sympetrum* species and the delicate Blue-Tailed Damselfly *Ischnura elegans* during its immature phase, sunning themselves on brambles.

Despite the fact that some species spend most of their time away from water, ponds and lakes are the best places to see dragonflies. It is in association with open water that the greatest number of species and individuals may be seen. At a large, unpolluted lowland pond, one would expect to see at least half a dozen species occupying different niches. The metallic-green and powder-blue Emerald Damselfly *Lestes sponsa* may be seen fluttering among the reeds and rushes or sunning itself with characteristically half-open wings, while swarms of mostly male blue damselflies, such as the Common Blue *Enallagma cyathigerum*, fly close to the surface of open water. Along the bank, the male Black-Tailed Skimmer *Orthetrum cancellatum* or, later in the year, the red Common Darter *Sympetrum striolatum*, will be found sunning itself on a dry reed, or more often these days on a discarded white sandwich wrapper. The Brown Hawker *Aeshna grandis* is a large and powerful brown dragonfly with ginger-coloured wings, which has a preference for hawking well out over the open water at a height of three metres or more. The Southern Hawker *A. cyanea* is more likely to swoop back and forth over a reedbed or under nearby trees. It may even hover quite close to the observer. A dark damselfly with a blue 'tail' marking seen flying between emergent vegetation will probably be the Blue-Tailed Damselfly *Ischnura elegans*, one of the commonest and most widespread in Britain, able to tolerate slightly more pollution than many other species.

A different set of species will be found at heathland ponds or boggy moor where the water is acidic. The Common Hawker *Aeshna juncea* may be seen patrolling along the edge of upland pools. The Black Darter *Sympetrum danae* and the Keeled Skimmer *Orthetrum coerulescens* are typical acid bog dragonflies. The Small Red Damselfly *Ceriagrion tenellum* is restricted to the same habitat.

Certain species, such as the tropical-looking metallic-coloured damselflies Beautiful Demoiselle *Calopteryx virgo* and Banded Demoiselle *C. splendens*, have a distinct preference for flowing water, the former being found over clear, stony-bottomed streams, while the latter is associated with muddy rivers and canals. The large yellow and black-banded Golden-Ringed Dragonfly *Cordulegaster boltonii* is frequently seen, one male to every twenty metres in favourable sites, patrolling up and down mountain streams. The Club-Tailed Dragonfly *Gomphus vulgatissimus* and the Hairy Dragonfly *Brachytron pratense* are two species most often found over lowland rivers, but are nowhere common.

Very little is known about how dragonflies select their habitat. We do not know whether it is cues such as rippling water or shiny surfaces that make a dragonfly home in on the habitat for which it is best adapted. Research has found that the White-Faced Dragonfly *Leucorrhinia dubia* has a preference for acidic bog water over tap water and that it is attracted to black patches with a white surround (a peat pool with dried sphagnum moss edging it has these characteristics and is the preferred breeding site). Very often when a dragonfly visits water for the first time, it will dip its abdomen in, as if to test that its eyes have correctly recognized open water. The Common Hawker *Aeshna juncea* and other species have been seen testing for water in this manner over dry tarmac roads. The presence of marginal or emergent green vegetation seems to be an important requirement for some of the *Sympetrum* species,

which will not remain long at ponds that have been tidied up.

The ideal site for many species would be a stretch of unpolluted water stocked with pondweed, with emergent vegetation along the shallow banks. Nearby there would have to be trees to act as a shelter and a large area of wild herbage or grass as a feeding area. Nitrate fertilizers, if they seep into open water, will encourage duckweed and algal slime, with the result that light is excluded and life ceases.

A watery patch among sphagnum moss and sedges in an acid bog. A good habitat for *Sympetrum danae*, *Somatochlora arctica*, *Ceriagrion tenellum*, *Orthetrum coerulescens*, *Leucorrhinia dubia* and *Aeshna juncea*.

A lowland river, well vegetated with yellow waterlilies and bur-reed. A good habitat for *Libellula fulva*, *Brachytron pratense*, *Coenagrion puella* and *Platycnemis pennipes*.

A lowland gravel pond in Epping Forest, sheltered by trees and well-stocked with emergent and floating vegetation. Over sixteen species recorded here, including *Aeshna cyanea*, *A. grandis*, *A. mixta*, *Anax imperator*, *Cordulia aenea*, *Erythromma najas*, *Pyrrhosoma nymphula* and *Sympetrum striolatum*.

Conservation

Considering the popularity of lakes and rivers for leisure activities, one would have thought that dragonfly habitats were quite secure from destruction. Angling is our most popular participatory sport, with over 3 million people involved, and at any site where there are dragonflies, one can be sure the water is unpolluted enough for fish. The more species of dragonfly there are present, the better a place is for fishing. The larvae do eat fish fry, but in turn they provide food for fish higher up the food chain. Birdwatchers consider lakes, rivers and marshes ideal places to see a wide variety of species, so they could be added to the many people who have an interest in preserving countryside that is also suitable for dragonflies. To this list we could add those who enjoy boating, canal travel and a walk around the local park pond.

Despite all the interest in and appreciation of our natural environment and its waterways, some of the most threatened habitats in Europe are the wetlands. In the past forty years, one new species, *Coenagrion scitulum*, has been discovered in Britain and another, *C. lunulatum*, in Eire, but in the same period three species have become extinct (*C. scitulum* again, *C. armatum*, and *Oxygastra curtisii*) and at least a third of the remaining species are considered to be rare and localized. The reasons for this are numerous. Our rivers may become polluted by industrial effluent that wipes out all the dragonfly larvae, when there are no sites nearby to replenish the stock. The most obvious example of this is the loss of the Orange-Spotted Emerald *Oxygastra curtisii*. The building of a housing estate in Hampshire destroyed its last remaining site. It was never common in Britain and the nearest site is now in southern France. The pollution and disturbance of water by too many cruisers on the Norfolk Broads probably contributed to the extinction of the Norfolk Blue Damselfly *Coenagrion armatum* and the loss of other species from the area. The nearest breeding site today is too far away across the North Sea for re-colonization to occur. Very often, local sites are destroyed by well-intentioned owners cleaning up a pond to make it more attractive for humans to look at, but, at the same time, driving out those species that like lush emergent vegetation in which to hide. Although some ponds do silt up and fill in with acidic autumn leaves, conservationists and landowners need to strike a balance when protecting suitable dragonfly habitats.

Some species are protected by law, such as the Norfolk Hawker *Aeshna isosceles*, but there is virtually no effective protection of the habitats on which they depend for breeding. Our wetlands are disappearing forever at an alarming rate because of the lack of legal protection, even for sites of special scientific interest (S.S.S.I.). Indeed, the farming industry can obtain government grants to drain land for planting wheat, despite the presence of a grain surplus in the E.E.C. It is of the utmost importance, therefore, to ensure that suitable sites are identified and preserved from interference. There are many ways in which individuals can help. The Biological Records Centre at the Institute of Terrestrial Ecology in Huntingdon* issues record cards and is involved in producing an invertebrate site register in conjunction with the British Dragonfly Society,† which itself produces an excellent journal and regular newsletters, as well as organizing field meetings for anyone interested in dragonflies. Local natural

* The Biological Records Centre, The Institute of Terrestrial Ecology, Monks Wood Experimental Station, Abbots Ripton, Huntingdon, Cambs, PE17 2LS.

† The Secretary – Mr R. H. Dunn, British Dragonfly Society, 4 Peakland View, Darley Dale, Matlock, Derbyshire, DE4 2GF.

history societies and conservation groups are also important watchdogs on changes in neighbourhood habitats.

It has been suggested that insect collectors are to blame for the loss of our rare species, but the main threat to the survival of dragonflies comes from the lack of protection of their habitat. Some of our very rare and localized species may be threatened by collectors, but over the country as a whole, entomologists are low down on the list of dangers.

Many people have not thought about the connection between the loss of dragonfly and other wildlife habitats and the essential needs of our own species – clean air and unpolluted water. What is urgently needed is the political will to protect and enhance the environment for all.

Dragonflies are not a serious threat to us; in their adult stage they must consume vast quantities of gnats, mosquitoes and other irritating insects and as larvae be a source of food to fish stocks, even if fish fry do get eaten in turn. Their main value to us is as a sign of unpolluted countryside and as attractive living creatures. In the end, I would argue that we do not have the right to destroy other species and their habitats, whether they are 'useful' to us or not.

Observation and Study

There is still considerable basic information about the ecology and behaviour of dragonflies that could be collected by dedicated amateurs. By sending records of sightings to the Biological Records Centre, it is possible to help in the study of distribution and population dynamics. Careful records over a number of years could tell an individual researcher or a local society about the changes in population or dates of emergence, perhaps related to climatic fluctuations. It is possible to put coded marks on dragonflies' wings, using a quick-drying felt-pen marker. Care must be taken not to damage the insect while marking, particularly the delicate damselflies. The effect of pollution on the numbers of dragonflies on a given stretch of water is also much in need of study. Simple tests are available, such as pH paper to measure the acidity of water, and Richard Mabey's *Pollution Handbook* is a good beginners' guide. We do not have detailed accounts of the behaviour of many species. Even the daily pattern of activity or precise accounts of pairing and ovipositing may be unrecorded. Any careful observations can be sent to the journal of the British Dragonfly Society.

In order to study dragonflies, a few basic items of equipment are necessary. First, a large net with which to catch specimens for closer identification is essential. Some people use a kite-shaped butterfly net made of cane and brass, with a black muslin bag, others prefer a net with an aluminium folding rim and dark nylon netting. If you intend to make a net, it is important to give it a rounded shape, without any corners where an insect can trap itself. The net should be fairly deep, because the technique for catching a dragonfly consists of a fast sweep, followed by a twist of the wrist to ensure that the captive insect remains trapped in the end of the bag. The Anisoptera are usually very swift in their flight, making it fruitless to chase after them. The best strategy is carefully to observe a dragonfly's behaviour and then either slowly move in close or stand motionless and wait until it flies near enough to sweep. Great patience is required to catch the most powerful fliers. Darter dragonflies, which regularly return to a favoured perch after a brief flight, may be attracted nearer if the observer places a light-coloured object, such as a paper handkerchief, on the ground, as they seem to prefer something light on which to sun themselves. In comparison, most of the Zygoptera are fairly easy to catch, because of their weaker flight. Care must be taken not to tear the voluminous net on brambles or dried twigs, but a needle and thread can always be carried for such an event. Having caught a dragonfly, it is best to grip a specimen with the wings held over its shoulders to prevent its struggling or being damaged by the fingers.

Captured damselflies can be observed in small test-tubes that are narrow enough to prevent fluttering of wings against the sides. A hand-lens comes in useful when looking at the prothorax, wing venation or abdominal markings. Larger species may be kept quiet in an envelope or folded paper protected by an old tobacco tin or suchlike. However, it is important to release them as soon as possible, into precisely the same sort of habitat from which they were captured. The best time to look for dragonflies at ponds is from mid morning onwards, bearing in mind that cold, wet and windy weather will keep them hidden, roosting in dense vegetation.

A pair of close-focus binoculars comes in very handy to search round a large lake without walking, and to identify dragonflies in inaccessible spots or when you do not wish to disturb them. A camera can provide a useful record of suitable habitats or evidence of pollution, as well as close-up shots of dragonflies in their natural surroundings. Sensible waterproof footwear is obviously important and in some circumstances a pair of large boots or waders comes in handy.

Collecting Larvae

The life history of a dragonfly makes for a fascinating study. The eggs may be collected from an ovipositing female if she can be induced to drop them into a test-tube of water or lay them in a reed stem, but as ideal conditions are needed for the eggs, and young larvae are difficult to maintain, many people prefer to collect larvae at a later stage in their metamorphosis. Larvae may be collected from weedy ponds, muddy bogs or the gravel in streams, depending on the species. A small, tough fishing net made of white cotton can be used to sample the water. A wire dredge or rake is helpful for pulling up clumps of pondweed for inspection. A large sheet of white polythene can be spread out on the bank, or a large plastic dish used to inspect weeds and detritus. Many of the larvae will remain still for some time when caught and even feign death if picked up; do not be deceived.

Larvae may be kept in small aquaria well stocked with material from their favoured habitat. They will need plenty of live food, from daphnia to other insect larvae and tadpoles. The larger Aeshnidae can be fed on live fish bait. If the tank becomes overcrowded and food scarce, the larvae will resort to cannibalism. When your interest in them has been satisfied, they can be returned to their original habitat. If the larvae are retained, then it is obviously important to provide suitable sites for use when they are ready to emerge and metamorphose. The impending transformation can often be predicted when a fully grown larva is seen clinging to a near-vertical stem just below the water surface. The actual emergence is well worth watching for the remarkable transformation that takes place, but it may mean losing a night's sleep or getting up very early to catch the initial stages.

The discovery of exuviae, or dried larval skins, at a site is clear evidence of breeding having taken place. It is possible to collect exuviae and preserve them in a box containing a sachet of naphthalene to prevent decomposition. The skin can be glued to a piece of card once the legs, labium and lamellae have been softened in water and spread out. The lamellae can be mounted separately between 35 mm. glass slide mounts and projected on to a screen for easy examination.

There is no section in this book on preserving dead specimens, for a variety of reasons. To begin with, entomological collections are a minority interest, probably best left to museums and specialists. Any encouragement to kill dragonflies might lead irresponsible individuals to pursue certain species for their rarity value. This cannot be condoned, given the precarious nature of so many dragonfly populations. Just as with birdwatching, interest has shifted from collecting to other involvements, such as ecology, behavioural studies and photography. These activities can only serve to increase our knowledge of dragonflies and, in turn, help to argue for their preservation.

BRITISH DRAGONFLIES

Male Scarce Emerald Damselfly (*Lestes dryas*)

Banded Demoiselle

Mature male

Pair mating

Average length 45 mm.
Average wingspan: male 61 mm., female 65 mm.

Both of the *Calopteryx* damselflies found in Britain are startling in the jewel-like bodies and iridescent wings. The aptly named *splendens* male has distinctive wing patches of deep purple or prussian blue that flash in the sunlight as the damselfly flutters over the water or displays to a passing female. The latter can be distinguished from the similar female Beautiful Demoiselle *C. virgo* by the coarser green venation of the translucent wings.

Description

The head, thorax and abdomen of the male are principally metallic ultramarine blue, with bottle-green sides to the thorax and tip of the abdomen. The eyes are dark red and there is a chrome-yellow labrum with a spot either side of it. The legs are black and bristly. The wings of the male are clear at the tips and base with a band down the centre that matures from brown to blue and purple. There is no pterostigma and the veins are not as fine as those of the Beautiful Demoiselle *C. virgo*. The upper claspers are black, incurved and flattened at the tip whereas the lower pair are flat, upturned and only half as long.

Great care should be taken to distinguish the two *Calopteryx* females. In the Banded Demoiselle *C. splendens* the female is mainly metallic emerald green turning bronze-red at the tip of the abdomen, which also has a yellow line down the centre of the last three segments. There are also some yellow markings along the side of the thorax and abdomen. The wings are translucent with metallic green veins unlike the pinky fawn veins of *C. virgo*. The white false pterostigma is twice as large on the forewings.

Larva Average length 30–45 mm.
The red-brown to dark green hairless larva is long and slender with long thin legs. It has a small head and a wide cleft in the labium. The caudal lamellae

Mature female   Mature female

are dark with two pale bands about midlength; the middle lamella is distinctly longer. The larva can be found in the sediment or between root stems searching for prey with its long antennae. This species has a preference for sluggish streams and canals. The larva usually takes two years to mature.

Behaviour and Habitat

The Banded Demoiselle requires a muddy bottom for the larvae and emergent or floating vegetation for the males to display on, as well as open meadows nearby for feeding grounds. It is most often seen along unpolluted slow-moving rivers and canals, occasionally by a pond. Its habitat requirements overlap with the Beautiful Demoiselle *C. virgo*, though the latter has a preference for swifter, more acid, streams with stony bottoms.

It is one of the few species in the British Isles to have a distinctive male courtship display. Perching on a prominent reed or a lily pad and defending the immediate area from rivals quite vigorously, the male reacts to a visiting female by spreading its iridescent wings and raising the abdomen

slightly. If the female lands nearby, a courtship dance is performed. The male flies back and forth, always orientating his face towards her; in this way he can display his metallic colours to the best advantage. The male then lands on the female and grasps her prothorax with his claspers, and they fly off in tandem to the surrounding vegetation. Sperm is transferred to the accessory genitalia by the male and he touches her head with these organs. Both then bend their abdomens to form the mating wheel. Some minutes later the pair flies back to the egg-laying site, they separate, and the solitary female inserts eggs into plant tissue above and below water level.

Distribution and Time of Appearance

Relatively common where found on unpolluted muddy rivers in England, Wales and Ireland. Common throughout Europe and beyond as far as Siberia and China.

Seen between May and September, but most common in June, July and August.

Beautiful Demoiselle

Mature male

Immature male (note translucent brown wings at this stage)

Average length 45 mm.
Average wingspan: male 58 mm., female 63 mm.

This must be the most exotic-looking damselfly in Britain. Groups of males delicately flutter like inky blue butterflies over stony brooks and rivers in midsummer. The females that feed in the adjacent meadows are almost as eye-catching; emerald-green bodies tipped with bronze-red, and translucent wings tinged in gold and pink. The wing colour in the female and the extent of the dark areas on the male wings help distinguish this species from the Banded Demoiselle *C. splendens* and the wing veins are more dense in both sexes. Both species favour clean rivers that flow through open grassland, bordered by trees. The Beautiful Demoiselle frequents stony-bottomed, more acidic waters whereas the Banded Demoiselle is more often seen along muddy rivers.

Description
The mature male is almost entirely metallic blue, with the exception of a yellow labrum and a spot either side of the frons, and dark red eyes. In addition, the long bristly legs are black as are the anal appendages. The upper appendages are curved inwards while the shorter lower ones curve up and slightly towards one another. The dark area of the wings reaches almost to the base and wingtips. It is translucent brown to begin with, but darkens to almost black, shot with purple, green and prussian blue.

The female is metallic green on the head, thorax and abdomen, turning bronze-red near the tip. There are yellow markings along the side of the thorax and abdomen as well as a yellow line down the centre of the last three segments. The wing veins are pink and the overall tint is light brown, marked by a white false pterostigma.

Larva Average length 30–35 mm.
The eggs hatch soon after being laid and the larva grows for two years among the silt and weeds of fast-flowing clear rivers. A long, rather spidery-legged larva with a small head and long antennae used for tracking prey. The labium is deeply cleft, more so than *C. splendens*. The caudal lamellae have a single light band; the middle lamella is slightly shorter and more leaf-like than the other two.

Mature female

Mature female

Behaviour and Habitat

The preferred habitat requirements are a clean fast-flowing river with a stony bed, and trees sheltering the banks. Nearby meadowland or herbage is important as a feeding place. This species has been seen in less favourable sites such as those frequented by *C. splendens*, canals, muddy rivers and ponds.

In the early morning males fly over the vegetation near the river feeding on the rich insect life. As the day heats up, single males move to the river and establish small territories, which they survey from a prominent alder twig or bladed rush. Intruders are threatened by a flick of the wings or an actual pursuit out over the water. At the same time non-territorial males will patrol and fly in swarm groups without much sign of overt threat. They may even perch communally and show no inter-male aggression.

When a female is ready to pair she will visit the riverside and perch prominently on emergent vegetation. The courting male hovers round her before settling in front and eventually pairing up. After many minutes the female separates and flies down to the water to lay eggs in stems and leaves below the surface. The male may sit nearby and chase off other curious males, both partners occasionally flicking their wings to each other. If the male approaches and tries to interrupt her ovipositing she will flash open her wings and raise her abdomen slightly as a threat gesture.

Distribution and Time of Appearance

Distribution is strongly determined by suitable riverine habitats, which are more frequently encountered in the south-west of England, Wales, the Lake District, western Scotland and southern Eire. World distribution stretches across Europe to China and Japan; in some places local subspecies have been named.

An early damselfly that is on the wing from May to September in good years, most often seen in June and July.

Scarce Emerald Damselfly

Mature male

Pair in tandem searching for a suitable egg-laying stem

Average length: male 37 mm., female 34 mm.
Average wingspan 20–25 mm.

Once thought to be extinct, this species has been rediscovered breeding in East Anglia after a lapse of a few years. Its favoured habitat of choked drainage ditches and weedy pools has made it vulnerable to land reclamation schemes, a recent change in land use which has robbed us of some of the best wet meadows and marshes. Even so, it is not a conspicuous creature when fluttering from stem to stem among close-growing vegetation. In the places where it breeds, this species may have been overlooked on account of its close similarity with the much more common and widespread *L. sponsa*. The introduction to that species, and the key, should help to distinguish the two Emerald damselflies.

Two other *Lestes* species occur on the British List on the basis either of sightings on the Channel Isles or of a one-off record. The Shy Emerald *L. barbarus* (Fabricius 1798) is readily identified by the two-tone pterostigma of cream and light brown, whereas the Green Emerald *L. viridis* (van der Linden 1825) has a remarkably long thin abdomen, long male upper claspers and very short lower ones. It is worth mentioning at this point the related species Brown Emerald *Sympecma fusca* (van der Linden 1820), which is also on the British List. It looks like a brown *Lestes* in appearance and has the interesting distinction of overwintering as an adult, remaining hidden among dead leaves and stems during hibernation.

Description
The mature male has bright pale blue eyes and frons. The top of the thorax and abdomen are metallic green highlighted with bronze-red and when young the sides of the thorax and the underneath of the abdomen are yellow. With ageing the male becomes covered in a pale blue bloom on the prothorax and the yellow areas of the body as well as part of the second segment and the last three segments of the abdomen. The legs are black and yellow and the black claspers are diagnostic, the upper ones being incurved and flattened while the

Mature female

Mature female

lower ones are square-tipped and curved up and inwards. The clear wings have an oblong pterostigma which ages from yellow to black.

Immature males resemble the female, which has brown eyes and a yellow frons, and also two rectangular green spots on the second segment, which are a useful distinguishing characteristic. The yellow and green female looks stouter particularly towards the tip of the abdomen, which bears a large ovipositor. The anal appendages are short and pointed.

Larva Average length 29–32 mm.
The eggs overwinter and the larva grows rapidly before a summer emergence in the same year. A rather narrow, long-legged larva with a pale line along its back. It is very similar to *L. sponsa* but the labial palps on a long spoon-shaped labium have at least three bristles each. The weeds and stems of ditches and ponds are the typical habitat.

Behaviour and Habitat
This well-camouflaged damselfly keeps well down among the emergent vegetation of ditches and ponds, either settling on stems with wings half open, or flying swiftly between perches. It does seem to prefer more dense vegetation, even drier sites than *L. sponsa*.

After mating for some time, the pair fly in tandem to vertical sedge or rush stems to oviposit. The female begins about halfway down the stem, depositing one egg at a time and working downwards, sometimes inserting them below the water surface.

Distribution and Time of Appearance
Despite its very rare status it is probably more widespread than records show. In the past it has been seen along the eastern side of England from Lincolnshire to Kent and as far inland as the Cambridgeshire Fens. It also occurs at various sites in Ireland. Elsewhere it occurs across Europe (but never at high altitudes) to Siberia, and in North America.

It is most often seen in July and August.

Emerald Damselfly

Mature male

Mature male (note powder-blue on thorax and abdomen)

Average length 38 mm.
Average wingspan 36 mm.

The two Emerald damselflies are perhaps the hardest species to distinguish and to make matters more difficult they sometimes share the same habitat of lush emergent vegetation. The key summarizes the essential differences between them. Both males are emerald green and powder blue when mature, but *L. dryas* has brighter blue eyes and blunter lower claspers. The female *L. sponsa* is slimmer and has two teardrop-shaped emerald spots on the first abdominal segment (in *dryas* they are rectangular). The pterostigma of the Emerald Damselfly is slightly shorter. Both species have clear wings and are smaller than the two *Calopteryx* damselflies. One further characteristic

is the half-opened wings of a perched Emerald damselfly.

Description

The male is mostly metallic green tinged with bronze. The eyes and front of the head are light blue. The sides of the thorax and the underneath of the abdomen are initially yellow but become covered in a pale blue pruinescence with age as do the first, second, eighth, ninth and tenth abdominal segments. The legs are black and yellow as are the anal appendages. The upper ones curve round to meet each other and the lower pair are quite thin and round-tipped. The clear wings have black veins and pterostigmata that darken from yellow to black. Very teneral individuals sometimes show a multicolour sheen to the wings.

Young males are similar to females in colouring, they have yellow not blue on the head, and pale brown eyes. In some females the normally yellow areas on the thorax and abdomen are pink or beige. The ovipositor is quite distinctive but the anal appendages are small and pointed.

Mature female

Immature female

Mature female

Larva Average length 26·5–34·5 mm.
The eggs diapause so that the larva completes its growth within the space of two to five months in the spring and early summer. It lives among the weeds in ponds, drainage ditches and marshy pools. A slim-looking larva with long banded caudal lamellae and a ladle-shaped deeply cleft labium. The labial palps each have two bristles unlike the rarer *L. dryas* which has three.

Behaviour and Habitat
Both sexes may be seen fluttering between the upright stems of reeds, rushes and other emergent vegetation on the boggy surrounds to a lake, pond or canal, and are rarely seen out in the open. They can breed in acid bogs, brackish marshes and barely wet ditches.

    The pair mate among lush emergent vegetation before flying off in tandem to oviposit. The female works her way down a plant stem sometimes ending up completely submerged. The V-shaped incisions left by the ovipositor are in line down the stem.

Distribution and Time of Appearance
Widely distributed throughout the British Isles and fairly common where found. Its range extends across Europe between the Arctic and northern Italy to Asia.

    A late-summer damselfly seen between late June and September but most numerous in July and August.

White-Legged Damselfly

Mature male

Male (note the expanded white tibia, especially on the hind legs)

Average length 36 mm.
Average wingspan 45 mm.

A pale-looking damselfly that inhabits the sheltered herbage bordering muddy lowland rivers. It is vulnerable to pollution and thus a good indicator of a chemically clean river. The most distinctive feature of this species, and one which separates it from the blue *Coenagrion* damselflies, is the broad white tibia on the mid and hind legs. This characteristic of the genus has evolved into a means of communication functioning in courtship and aggressive encounters.

Description
Both sexes emerge a very pale creamy white, the degree of colour and black markings varying with age and between individuals. The mature male has a pattern of very pale blue and black lines. The tip of the abdomen is usually black broken by an irregular light stripe down the middle, ending with blue claspers. The lower pair forms a pincer shape extending beyond the triangular upper ones. The white legs have expanded tibia and a black line along the femur. The clear wings have yellow to pale brown pterostigmata.

The female is very similar in pattern to the male except that the light colouring is a pale green and the black areas are less extensive on the abdomen. On the sides of the thorax the hue blends into yellow. The female form known as *lactea* Charpentier has very reduced black markings, no more than tiny spots in some individuals, on a creamy white background blending to pale brown where the thoracic markings should be. The female appendages are short and pointed.

Typical female, pale green

Female form *lactea*, creamy-white with reduced black markings

Larva Average length 18·5–22 mm.
The larva lives on the river bed among mud, weeds and debris. It is slim with long bristly legs and elongated pointed caudal lamellae patterned in dark blotches. The labium has short bristles along each side. Emergence takes place after two years of larval growth.

Behaviour and Habitat
It is a local species found in colonies where the habitat is suitable. This is usually muddy rivers which are sheltered with plenty of lush vegetation along the banks and neighbouring meadows. Occasionally it is found on nearby ponds and lakes. Both sexes visit the water to rendezvous and males may be seen flying low over the surface in search of a suitable mate. The male grasps the female in flight after displaying his white legs. Pairing takes place on nearby vegetation and after some time they fly in tandem to oviposit in emergent or floating plants. The eggs are laid in a zigzag pattern round a stem below the water level but the female does not immerse her whole body during the process. The male remains attached, holding his body vertically up all the while.

Distribution and Time of Appearance
Locally common on many rivers from the Midlands southwards and in Wales. It has an extensive European distribution that only excludes the Iberian peninsula, northern Scandinavia, Ireland and Iceland. The range extends into the Middle East.

The flying season extends from June to August but it is most common at the end of June and in July.

Large Red Damselfly

Mature male

Male

Average length 36 mm.
Average wingspan: male 44 mm., female 48 mm.

A very common and widespread damselfly, which has been recorded from a wide variety of habitats over most of the British Isles. Apart from being larger it can readily be distinguished from the rare Small Red Damselfly *Coenagrion tenellum* by its hairy ridged frons, black legs, red (or yellow) shoulder stripes and, in the male at least, bronze-black patches on the abdomen. Care should be taken not to confuse the dark form of the female with the Red-Eyed Damselfly *Erythromma najas*, which has blue joints between segments eight and ten.

Description

The head is black on top with a red frons striped in black hairy lines. The eyes are crimson in the male. The thorax is bronze-black on top with two red shoulder stripes. Below a red side stripe the thorax is yellow lined in black. The red areas mature from orange and yellow. The legs are black. Up to the sixth segment, the abdomen is crimson banded with bronze, the seventh and onwards are mostly bronze marked with red. The upper appendages are split, while the lower pair are conical. The wings are clear and the pterostigma is light brown and black.

There are three female forms. The most common has similar markings to the male with the addition of an extra band and dorsal line of bronze-black along the second to sixth abdominal segments. Immature females are yellow and bronze. The second form, *melanotum* Selys, has yellow shoulder stripes and abdominal joints, and the rest of the top of the abdomen is bronze. If the bronze-black abdominal markings are reduced, this is the third form, known as *fulvipes* Stephens. The female claspers are short and red.

Female, typical form

Female

Larva Average length 19–22.5 mm.

The eggs hatch soon after being laid. An easily identifiable larva. The stumpy body bears a large rectangular head and three broad caudal lamellae marked with a dark X-shape. There is a pale line edged by dark pigment along the top of the abdomen. It is able to survive among the mud and debris in a variety of habitats, both acid and alkali, still and moving, even brackish marshes. After nearly two years' growth the larva spends the winter in diapause. Emergence is synchronized into a series of peaks beginning in early spring. It takes place in the early morning among the grass along the banks.

Behaviour and Habitat

The males are quite aggressive and will attack one another, and even a perched male White-Faced Dragonfly. The warm part of midday is spent flying along the edge of marginal vegetation, feeding or searching for visiting females. After mating among nearby vegetation the pair remain in tandem as the female lays eggs in submerged vegetation.

It lives in a variety of wetland habitats ranging from moorland bog to lowland lakes, rivers and canals as well as brackish water. Most common near sheltered, unpolluted water that is well vegetated.

Distribution and Time of Appearance

A widespread distribution throughout the British Isles and most of mainland Europe as far as northern Scandinavia and Russia, also occurring in Asia Minor.

Common in May, June and July, sometimes into August.

Blue-Tailed Damselfly

Mature male

Average length 31 mm.
Average wingspan 35 mm.

This very common damselfly breeds in a variety of habitats and is able to survive in mildly polluted water. It is found throughout the British Isles except the north-east of Scotland, where winter temperatures presumably prevent successful breeding. Paradoxically, the adult can be seen flying on cool windy days when other species have gone to a sheltered roost. Despite the bewildering variety of female forms there are only two species it may be confused with. The Scarce Blue-Tailed Damselfly *I. pumilio* is smaller; the male has different blue markings on the abdomen, the female in the typical form has lime to olive-green eye spots and sides to the thorax. The Blue-Tailed Damselfly *I. elegans* has a raised centre lobe to the prothorax absent in the rarer relative. The Red-Eyed Damselfly *Erythromma najas* has different coloured eyes, and no eye spots or thoracic stripes, and the blue of the male is distributed differently (see the key).

Description

The male has only one colour form although the light areas on the head and thorax develop from light green to turquoise blue. The eyes are green-blue and the top of the head is black, with two large blue eye spots. The prothorax has a pointed raised centre lobe. The thorax is black on top except for two blue shoulder stripes, the sides are also blue. The legs are black on top, pale blue underneath. The top of the abdomen is black (slightly metallic green in strong light) except for the first and eighth segments which are blue; the first has a black square in the centre of it. Each of the joints is marked in yellow. The lower claspers are black and curved; above them are two small rounded upper claspers and a projection from the last segment. The clear wings have diamond-shaped pterostigmata, those of the forewings are black on one half, clear distally. The hind pterostigmata are pale brown with a dark area in the centre.

There are a number of female varieties; some intergrade or change into others. The andromorph develops colours just like the male changing from

Ischnura elegans (VAN DER LINDEN 1823)

Immature male with green colouring

Female form *infuscans*

Female form *infuscans-obsoleta*

Female form *violacea*

Mature pair mating, female with typical blue colouring

green to blue with age. The form *violacea* Selys has a violet thorax but is otherwise identical to the andromorph. This variety may acquire a blue thorax or turn into *infuscans* Campion, which has olive-green eye spots and thoracic colouring in place of blue; the eighth segment is brown. The form *rufuscens* Stephens has blue, orange or pink eye spots, and an orange to salmon pink thorax with only a narrow black band along the top; the eighth segment is blue. *Infuscans-obsoleta* Killington develops dull yellow or light brown eye spots and thorax and a brown eighth segment from *rufuscens* colours and patterning.

All the females have short anal appendages, and pterostigmata like those of the male hindwing.

Larva Average length 21·5–25 mm.
Eggs hatch after about three weeks. The slim larva lives among weeds in ponds, slow rivers and brackish marshes; it is less common in acid waters. The caudal lamellae are pointed and leaf-like with a hairy fringe distal to the wavy-lined node. See the key to distinguish this species from *I. pumilio*. Growth is completed in one year.

Habitat and Behaviour
It is tolerant of brackish water but is most common in neutral to alkali-rich waters with plenty of marginal vegetation. It does not fly out over open water much but prefers to weave among emergent reeds and rushes, settling frequently. A perched individual will give a threat display by opening its wings and raising the abdomen. When two males meet in flight they face one another and bob up and down rapidly, the more vigorous one tending to dominate.

Pairing takes place at the water's edge and the pair fly in the wheel position to marginal vegetation. Copulation frequently lasts three hours and often longer, suggesting that sperm displacement takes place. The female oviposits alone placing eggs individually into submerged vegetation. If she is disturbed and does not want to pair the end of the abdomen is held down as a signal to the male.

Distribution and Time of Appearance
Widely distributed throughout the British Isles but most common in the south. It occurs across the Continent, excluding northern Scandinavia, to the Middle East and across Russia to China.

There is a bimodal emergence occurring in June and then in July and August. It may be seen earlier or later according to conditions.

Female form *rufuscens*

Scarce Blue-Tailed Damselfly

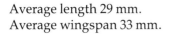
Mature male

Mature male

Average length 29 mm.
Average wingspan 33 mm.

It is likely that this small and secretive damselfly has been overlooked in some parts of the British Isles. The most promising sites seem to be eutrophicated acid pools and seepages, but these are vulnerable to drainage schemes and it is hoped that more protection will be given to these habitats. One of the female varieties is bright orange over most of the head, the thorax and some of the wing veins and is unlikely to be mistaken for anything else. The typical female form and the male are similar to the Blue-Tailed Damselfly *I. elegans*, although smaller. The key summarizes the major differences. Note which segment is blue in the male, and in both sexes note whether the prothorax has a raised centre lobe.

Description
The male has a black top to the head, green-blue on the eye spots and rest of the head. Mature individuals have two blue shoulder stripes on a black top to the thorax, the sides are a similar blue. The legs are black above, blue below. The top of the abdomen is black except for part of the eighth and all of the ninth segments. There is some blue on the sides of these segments as well as the first, second and tenth segments. The upper anal appendages are short and rounded, the lower

Female, typical form (note browny-green thorax)

Female form *aurantiaca* (note orange colouring)

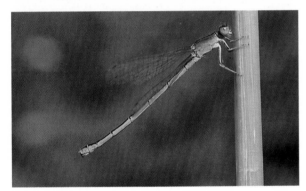

Mature female, typical form

Larva Average length 15–20 mm.
The eggs hatch soon after being laid and the larva probably takes two years to develop among the debris in boggy pools and sluggish streams or ditches. It is similar to the more common species although smaller; refer to the key for details. The short caudal lamellae have marginal hairs, distal to the uneven node.

Behaviour and Habitat
This species spends most of the time low down among emergent vegetation in boggy areas near shallow pools, slow streams and runnels. It is more tolerant of acidic waters than *I. elegans*, although it can breed in alkaline water too. After pairing among the vegetation, the female flies off to lay eggs in plant stems growing in shallow or muddy water. Sometimes the male remains to guard her.

Distribution and Time of Appearance
Records have been given for a variety of sites at one time or another, most of them in the south of England, Wales and the west of Ireland. It is found across Europe, excluding Scandinavia, to the Middle East and Asia.

On the wing from the end of May to the end of July.

ones curve inwards like pincers. The clear wings have squarish pterostigmata; those on the forewings are larger and two-toned grey and white, more distinctly so in the male.

The typical female has light areas which mature from yellow through lime green to olive brown and finally black. The markings are similar to the male except that the shoulder stripes are less distinct and the top of the abdomen is entirely black. The female variety *aurantiaca* Selys is bright orange on the head, the thorax (except a central black line), the top of the first few segments and the last segment. The sides and some of the wing veins are also orange. The rest of the abdomen is black.

Northern Blue Damselfly

Mature male

Mature male (note second segment markings joined in this individual)

Average length 31 mm.
Average wingspan 40 mm.

A very rare and localized damselfly that has only been recorded in Scotland. It is probably an Ice Age relic left behind in pockets of subarctic-like habitat such as acid bog pools found in Caledonian pine forests. It looks similar to the Irish Blue *C. lunulatum*; both males have green-blue on the thorax and a black dash on either side of segment two, but the *C. lunulatum* male has a darker abdomen, and has only been recorded in Ireland. The prothorax and anal appendages are the best determining features (see the key). The Northern Blue

has the typical *Coenagrion* characteristics of thin shoulder stripes and two short lines on the side of the thorax, and the absence of an eighth segment apical spine in the female, to distinguish it from the Common Blue *Enallagma cyathigerum*, which sometimes shares the same habitat.

Description

The male is primarily black and light blue with a touch of green on the sides of the thorax and head. Immature males are lilac and black. The top of the head is black with two eye spots and a line between them in blue. The eyes are blue-green. The prothorax has a light-coloured posterior edge and

Mature female

Female

a midpoint which is only slightly raised. The thorax has two light shoulder stripes and two short black lines on the sides as in other *Coenagrions*. The abdomen is sky blue marked with bronze-black on each segment except the eighth and ninth. The second segment has a black line on each side flanking a spearhead design. This last feature may be reduced to a spot or line, or expanded to join up with the side markings. The upper appendages form two very short, rounded projections; the lower pair form two short, inwardly pointing hooks. The wings are clear with black pterostigmata.

The pale blue of the male's head and thorax is replaced by green in the female; this progressively darkens with age. The female abdomen is almost entirely bronze-black edged in green. The claspers form two conical points.

Larva Average length 21–23 mm.
The eggs hatch soon after being laid, development usually taking a year. The slim larva lives among the debris in bog pools and mountain lakes. The caudal lamella has a blunt tip and a node which

runs straight between a notch on each side. The head has two spots behind the prominent eyes unlike the Common Blue *Enallagma cyathigerum*.

Behaviour and Habitat
Females and immatures keep to nearby marshy areas, flying low down among the vegetation. When the sun comes out the males swarm by the water's edge keeping close to the surface. They are found at sphagnum bog pools, acidic marshes and shallow lakes. Mating takes place among marginal vegetation where the female oviposits. The male remains in tandem as the female goes below the surface.

Distribution and Time of Appearance
Only recorded in a few localities in the Scottish Highlands and on Deeside. It has a scattered boreo-alpine distribution on the Continent, most often seen in the Pyrenees, the Alps and northern countries.

On the wing between late May and the beginning of August.

Irish Blue Damselfly

Mature male (note second segment markings)

Mature male

Average length 31 mm.
Average wingspan 40 mm.

This species was discovered in Ireland for the first time in 1981, an indication of how little is known about dragonfly distribution. On the Continent it sometimes shares the same habitat as the Northern Blue C. *hastulatum*, peaty pools and bog. It also looks similar to this species, particularly if a male Northern Blue *hastulatum* has reduced markings on segment two. The abdomen is more black than blue in the male and both sexes have a raised squarish lobe on the posterior margin of the prothorax, unlike similar species. The green-blue thorax on the male is quite distinctive in flight.

The Norfolk Blue Damselfly C. *armatum* (Charpentier 1840) is a northern European species that was last recorded on the Norfolk Broads in 1957. It is assumed that pollution destroyed the last remaining colony. The male has long flipper-like claspers and no shoulder stripes. It also has a black top to the abdomen except for some blue on segments two, eight and nine. Segment two has a dash on each side like the Irish Blue *lunulatum* but only a thick spot on top. The female prothorax has a large round midpoint projection with bumps either side. The dark abdomen has some light green on segments two and eight. On the last mentioned, the black mark has two lobes.

Coenagrion lunulatum (CHARPENTIER 1840)

Mature female

Female, colours not mature

Description

The top of the head in the male is black with two blue eye spots and a line between them. The eyes and rest of the head are grass green. The prothorax has a prominent squarish central lobe on the posterior margin. The thorax is black above with two blue shoulder stripes. The sides are sky blue grading into grass green marked by two short black lines. The legs are black above, green-blue below. The abdomen has more black than blue on top. Segment two has a black dash on each side and a crescent shape in the middle. The upper appendages are very short and blunt, the lower ones form thick blunt pincers divided into two projections. The wings are clear with black pterostigmata.

The light areas on the female head and thorax are light green turning to brown. The abdomen is nearly all bronze-black on top, the sides and joints are green-brown except for the eighth and ninth segments. The first half of the eighth segment and the ninth joint are sky blue. The anal appendages form two very short points.

Larva Average length 21–23 mm.

The larva inhabits peaty pools and lakes living among debris. It is slim and thin-legged. The caudal lamella has a notch halfway along at the node and marginal setae as far as the blunt tip.

Behaviour and Habitat

Males swarm in large numbers over open water in early summer, flying close to the surface. Females move through nearby grass and rushes, only coming to water to mate. Pairing takes place in marginal vegetation and egg-laying is performed in tandem. Eggs are inserted into the plant stems and leaves of aquatic vegetation. The preferred habitat is blanket bog, peat pools and eutrophicated acidic lakes.

Distribution and Time of Appearance

It has been recorded from a number of places in western and central Ireland. On the Continent it is local from the Massif Central to northern Europe. Its range extends across the U.S.S.R. to Asia.

A short flight period in June and early July only.

Southern Blue Damselfly

Mature male (note second segment markings)

Mature female

Average length 29 mm.
Average wingspan 35 mm.

A small and delicate blue damselfly restricted to coastal Wales and the south of England where it breeds in slow-moving, often calcareous streams. The male has a distinctive mercury sign on segment two; the prothorax and claspers should distinguish it from the Azure and Variable Blue Damselflies *C. puella* and *C. pulchellum*. The small round eye spots and small pterostigmata also distinguish both sexes from other blue-green and black damselflies.

The Dainty Blue Damselfly *C. scitulum* (Rambur 1842) became extinct in 1953 as a result of the sea flooding its only known breeding site, in Essex. It is similar to the Southern Blue *C. mercuriale* except that the pterostigma is oblong and sandy brown, and the prothorax has a raised central lobe on the posterior margin. The female has more light blue on the abdomen than *mercuriale*.

Description

The male develops from lilac to blue, and black. The eyes are light blue and the top of the head is black with two small round eye spots almost joined by a blue line. The prothorax has a shallow, almost straight, posterior edge. The thorax is black on top, broken by two thin blue shoulder stripes, and the sides have two short lines on a blue background. The abdomen is blue and black including segment two which has an inverted crescent joined to a mushroom shape by a vertical line. (Very rarely this line is missing.) The next segment has a thin spearhead shape in black. The upper appendages are divided into fine and blunt projections. The lower ones also have two projections; one is hooked, the other is short and rounded. The wings are clear with small black pterostigmata.

The light colouring in the female develops from pale yellow to either green or blue, becoming brown with age. The patterning is the same as the

Blue form of female

Green form of female

male on the head and thorax but the abdomen is very dark. Segment two has a thistlehead, all others are almost entirely black on top. The joints between the last few segments are blue. The light-coloured appendages are short and blunt.

Larva Average length 15–17 mm.
It inhabits the weeds of slow-moving unpolluted streams. Eggs hatch soon after being laid but growth usually takes two years. A typical *Coenagrion* larva with a light band down the top of the abdomen. The labium is short and broad and there are no spots behind the eyes. The caudal lamella is short and boat-shaped; it has a node running at right angles and long marginal hairs that reach to a pointed tip.

Behaviour and Habitat
The most suitable habitat occurs where a neutral to alkaline stream flows slowly through a boggy marshy area, low in nitrates. Well-vegetated runnels are also attractive. Both sexes have a rather feeble flight tending to keep among the grass and boggy vegetation bordering streams and rivers. Pairing is similar to other *Coenagrions* and the female will go below the water surface to lay eggs in floating or submerged vegetation. The male remains in tandem.

Distribution and Time of Appearance
A very rare damselfly with specific habitat requirements. It has been recorded from various localities in Wales and from Cornwall to Hampshire in the south of England. It is mainly a southern European species with a subspecies in Italy and another in North Africa, unable to spread further north than Holland.

Azure Damselfly

Mature male   Male (note second segment markings)

Average length 33 mm.
Average wingspan 41 mm.

A common damselfly on lakes and ponds in summer but not as widespread as the Common Blue *Enallagma cyathigerum*. Easily distinguished from the latter by the narrow blue shoulder stripes, black lines along the thorax and a U-shape on the male's second segment. The female lacks an apical spine. It is most likely to be confused with the Variable Blue *Coenagrion pulchellum* (pages 42–3) and the key should be closely studied. The prothorax and claspers are the best determining features because of the colour and pattern variations in both species.

Description

The light colouring in males develops from a pale lilac to sky blue. The top of the head is black with two pear-shaped eye spots and the prothorax has a slightly wavy posterior edge lined with blue. The top of the thorax has two narrow stripes and the sides have a short black line with a dash below it.

The legs are black and pale blue. The abdomen is sky blue and black; on the second segment there is a black U-shape, only rarely broken or joined to the line below it. The eighth segment is blue and so is part of the ninth. The upper appendages are blunt; the lower pair each have two projections, one of which curves inwards slightly. The wings are clear and the pterostigmata are black.

The female occurs in two basic forms. Both are similar to the male on the head and thorax, the light colour is pale green when mature. The green form has an almost entirely bronze-black top to the abdomen. There is a square-topped thistlehead on the second segment, and the tenth segment and the ends of the previous three segments are blue. The other joints and light areas along the sides are green. In the second form, *annulatum* Selys, the blue is more extensive, leading to confusion with the Variable Blue *C. pulchellum*. Sometimes the second segment's thistlehead is replaced by a thickened mercury sign similar to the Southern Blue *C. mercuriale*. The female appendages are black.

Female

Green form of female

Pair mating

Larva Average length 22–25·75 mm.
The larva inhabits weedy ponds, lakes and canals and takes one year to complete its growth. It has a slender body and thin legs, usually green with brown wing-sheaths. The large head has prominent spots behind the eyes. The caudal lamellae have a node running at right angles and only a slightly hairy edge to them. Usually the tips are blunt, but not always.

Behaviour and Habitat

Males like to swarm over floating vegetation or search marginal vegetation for food and females. They also sun themselves on broad leaves, deterring other males that fly too close by opening the wings and raising the abdomen slightly. Both sexes may also be found in wet meadows and marshland. After pairing in the usual manner they egg-lay in tandem on floating vegetation; sometimes the female disappears below the surface.

Distribution and Time of Appearance

Rare in Scotland, not found at all in the north-east, but common elsewhere in the British Isles. Found across Europe (except northern Scandinavia) as far as the Caspian Sea, and in North Africa.

Most common in June and July, but it can be found from May to September in favourable years.

Variable Blue Damselfly

Mature male (note second segment markings and broken blue lines on thorax top)

Male, with parasitic water mite larvae just visible underneath thorax

Average length 33 mm.
Average wingspan 42 mm.

The Variable Blue Damselfly lives up to its name because of differences in the degree of black. Dark males are easier to recognize but when the black areas are reduced the male may be confused with the Azure Damselfly *C. puella* and the female with the Southern Blue *C. mercuriale*. The dark form of the female is very much like the Azure Damselfly *C. puella* and often occurs where both species are present. The most confident discrimination can be made by checking for the deeply lobed posterior edge to the prothorax. The male claspers are also diagnostic; check the key.

Description

The male is black and sky blue (lilac in immature specimens). The top of the head is black with two blue eye spots, sometimes with a line between them. The prothorax has a blue edge and a spot on each side. Characteristically the posterior margin is shaped into three lobes; the central one bears a raised point. The top of the thorax is black, with markings that vary from two blue stripes to only small traces of light blue. The sides are light blue and marked by a short black line and a dash below that. The legs are black and pale blue. The second segment has a black U joined by a stem to the line below it (the stem may be absent leading to confusion with the Azure Damselfly *C. puella*). Usually

Female (note the extensive blue on abdomen in this form)

Mature female, darker form

Immature female, darker form

there is more black on the remaining segments than in the Azure Damselfly *C. puella*. Segment eight is entirely blue, nine has varying amounts of black. The upper claspers are broad and cream-tipped. The lower claspers have two points; the lower one is thick and conical while the upper one is thin and inward curving, as long as the upper claspers. The wings are clear with black pterostigmata.

There are two female forms. One is like the male on the head and thorax but the abdomen is a richer blue marked in black. The second-segment marking forms a thickened mercury sign and the tenth is black. The second form, *nigrescens* Puschnig, has an abdomen very much like the dark form of the Azure Damselfly *C. puella*. The second segment has a thistlehead while the rest is black except for light-coloured joints. The blue is replaced by green. The female appendages are short and pointed.

Larva Average length 20–25·25 mm.
The eggs hatch after about a month and growth is usually completed in a year. The larva looks very much like *C. puella* but is more often brown or sepia than green. The blunt lamellae have sparse hairs and a node running at right angles. The larva

also has spots behind the eyes like *puella*. Found in well-vegetated ponds and canals.

Behaviour and Habitat
It is like the Azure Damselfly *C. puella* in its behaviour and habitat choice, although it seems to have a preference for fenland. It develops to maturity among the herbage and grassy meadows bordering ponds, lakes and canals. The mature males swarm over open water during the sunniest part of the day. Pairing takes place on the water margins and egg-laying is performed in tandem. The male rests upright as the female inserts her eggs into water-lilies and other floating plants, sometimes forming concentric circles round a small perforation in a leaf.

Distribution and Time of Appearance
Locally abundant in many places but becoming scarce overall. More reliably seen in the south and east of England but there are records as far apart as Cornwall, Anglesey and Scotland. Its range extends from Ireland to Russia and beyond the Caspian Sea. Also found in Scandinavia and southwards down to Spain and Turkey.

Most common in June and July.

Common Blue Damselfly

Mature male (note second segment marking)

Male

Average length 32 mm.
Average wingspan 38 mm.

Males will swarm over open water facing the wind, sometimes on exposed lakes where no other damselfly can be seen. Females and immatures may be found in nearby grassland. It is a very common species found throughout the British Isles, possibly the most abundant damselfly in the world; its distribution stretches right round the northern hemisphere. It can be distinguished from the blue *Coenagrion* species by a variety of characteristics. The male has a blue shoulder stripe broader than the black line alongside it. In both sexes the sides of the thorax are marked only by a short line. The second segment on the male is diagnostic and only the Northern Blue *C. hastulatum* has both the eighth and ninth segments entirely blue. The female has an apical spine below, and an arrowhead mark on top of the eighth segment.

Description
The male is sky blue and black, slightly lilac when immature. Notable features are the large blue eye spots with a line between them, and a dorsal spot

Blue form of female

Blue form of female (note absence of long black markings on side of thorax and apical spine on segment eight)

on the prothorax. The thorax has broad shoulder stripes and a short black line low down on the sides. The legs are black above, pale below. The second segment has a black mushroom or oval spot, and the eighth and ninth segments are entirely blue. The black upper claspers are blunt, the lower ones are thin and curved. The wings are clear with black to brown pterostigmata.

Females occur in a variety of colour forms that can be grouped into two basic types. The green form develops from straw to grey-green marked with black. The second form changes from beige to pink, then lilac, finally sky blue and black. Both forms may turn brown and black with age. Note the thistlehead on the second segment and the arrowhead on the eighth, which also has an apical spine just behind the ovipositor. The female appendages are very reduced.

Larva Average length 20–26·5 mm.
A slim larva found among pondweed and debris, it varies in colour from black to green or yellow. The abdomen has a light spot surrounded by dark pigment on each segment. The caudal lamellae are leaf-like, pointed, and have a single dark band across the centre. Development usually takes one year.

Brown form of female

Olive-green form of female

Behaviour and Habitat

It is most often seen swarming low over open water at ponds, lakes, canals and slow streams, also found near brackish water. Pairing takes place on marginal vegetation and can last nearly an hour, though more often it takes about twenty minutes. During this time the male removes rival sperm and then deposits his own. Rival males who come too close are threatened by opening and raising the wings. The pair then fly to floating or emergent vegetation in tandem to search for suit-able oviposition sites. Sometimes the female ovi-posits when completely submerged and the male remains nearby to fight off intruding males. The longest recorded submergence is ninety minutes.

Distribution and Time of Appearance

Widely distributed throughout the British Isles, and across the Continent to the Middle East, the U.S.S.R. and China. It is also found in North America.

Common in June, July and August.

Males settled over water at communal rendezvous site

Red-Eyed Damselfly

Male (note ruby-red eyes)

Average length 35 mm.
Average wingspan: male 43 mm., female 46 mm.

Wherever a stretch of water in England has water-lilies or other floating plants it is worth looking for this attractive species. The males have grey, black and blue bodies when mature and distinctive large ruby eyes. Each individual will occupy a large leaf, occasionally flying fast and low over the water to chase other males or catch food. At first sight the male abdomen looks similar to that of the Blue-Tailed *Ischnura elegans* species but the blue areas are on the first, ninth and tenth segments only. There are no eye spots or blue shoulder stripes – another diagnostic feature. The only other confusion might be between a female of this species and the dark form of the female Large Red Damselfly, but the latter has yellow shoulder stripes and red markings.

Description

The mature male has a dark head with some orange on the frons and bright red eyes (brown and green when immature). The top of the thorax is a dark colour, highlighted a coppery red. The sides of the thorax, the wing joints, and the first, ninth and tenth segments are bright powdery blue. The rest of the abdomen is black, with light-coloured joints, gradually becoming steely grey-blue in maturity. The legs are black. The blue and black upper claspers are like two triangular pads; the lower ones are indistinct. The clear wings have pale brown pterostigmata.

The mature female has red eyes and a greenish dark top to the thorax with yellowy green sides. Occasionally some individuals have short yellow shoulder stripes. The whole of the top of the abdomen is greenish black with pale-coloured joints in the female. The anal appendages are short and pointed.

Larva Average length 29–32 mm.
This is a robust yet slim damselfly larva with blotched coloration. It lives among the weeds in ponds, lakes and slow-moving rivers and dykes. The caudal lamellae are the most distinctive features, each one has short marginal bristles from

Immature female

Mature male on lily pad (note grey-blue pruinescence (bloom) on abdomen)

Female

Female

the base to the node, then three dark bands terminating in a blunt tip. The head is broad with small eyes and a typical Coenagriid labium. Development usually takes one year.

Behaviour and Habitat

The main requirement of this species is the presence of floating vegetation such as water-lilies and *Potamogeton*. Males use the surface leaves as territorial sites (often some way from the shore) and the eggs are laid in submerged stems. Females and immature males may be seen away from the water in nearby fields or herbage, but the rendezvous sites for sexually mature individuals are ponds, lakes, slow rivers and canals. After mating in marginal vegetation the pair remains in tandem as the female oviposits into emergent and floating vegetation. Occasionally oviposition takes place below the surface, the female breathing from the silver bubble of air surrounding her body.

Distribution and Time of Appearance

Widespread and locally common in suitable habitats in the south and east of England. Its range extends into south Yorkshire and the Welsh border. Found in Europe from northern Scandinavia to the Mediterranean, extending its range as far as Siberia and Turkestan.

An early species seen most often in June and July, but in good weather a few weeks either side of these two months.

Small Red Damselfly

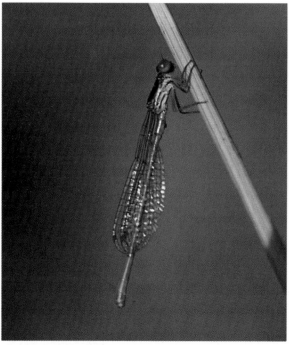

Male (note red legs)

Male

Average length 31 mm.
Average wingspan 36 mm.

The Small Red Damselfly is quite rare and restricted to clean acid bog in the south and west of Britain. Despite the bright red body it might not be noticed at first; it flies slowly, keeping low down between the rushes, and does not stray far from the breeding site. It can be distinguished from the Large Red by its smaller size, pale red legs and smooth frons. There are no shoulder stripes and the male has an entirely red abdomen.

Description

The male has a black and red head with crimson eyes. The thorax is dark bronze along the top and part-way down the sides where it becomes pale reddish yellow. The legs are light red and the abdomen is bright red terminating in very small hook-like claspers. The wings are clear with red-brown pterostigmata.

The female has three colour forms. The most common variety has a yellow to red line along the shoulder but otherwise the colouring of the head, thorax and legs is similar to the male's. The abdomen is partly red on the first to fourth segments, entirely bronze-black for the rest. The second variety, *erythrogastrum* Selys, is coloured entirely like the male and can be seen most often in the West Country. The third, *melanogastrum* Selys, is yellow on the head, thorax and sides of the abdomen where the other varieties are red. Each abdominal joint is marked in yellow but is otherwise black-bronze. The female also has small claspers.

Larva Average length 16–17 mm.
The eggs hatch soon after being laid and the larva usually takes two years to grow to full size. It lives in peaty bog pools and seepages on the muddy bottom. The caudal lamellae are distinctive; there are no setae beyond a wavy node although the edge is pigmented. The labium is short and usually has only two (sometimes four) premental setae. Overall the impression is of a slim larva with a large rectangular head and eyes and light spots along the top of the abdomen.

Female form *erythrogastrum*

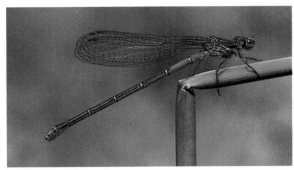

Female, typical form

Female, typical form

Female form *melanogastrum*

Behaviour and Habitat

Restricted in distribution to acid sphagnum bog, sluggish streams and runnels or pond margins with plenty of lush vegetation. Males remain in the colonial area, spacing themselves out through aerial conflicts. Individuals will rarely wander far, once mature. Pairing occurs near water from mid morning to late afternoon in fine weather. Mating is fairly long, from forty-five to ninety minutes, and takes place among marginal vegetation. The female lays eggs in submerged plant tissue while the male remains in tandem, holding his body upright throughout.

Distribution and Time of Appearance

Locally common in Wales and the south of England, in particular the increasingly threatened heathlands of Surrey, Sussex, Hampshire and Dorset. It has been recorded in East Anglia too. Found in North Africa and Europe northwards as far as Poland as well as in the Middle East.

Most often seen during June, July and August.

Club-Tailed Dragonfly

Male (note gap between the eyes)

Average length 50 mm.
Average wingspan 64 mm.

The Club-Tailed Dragonfly is a medium-sized black and yellow Hawker which breeds on a few unpolluted lowland rivers. It is unlikely to be confused with the much larger Golden-Ringed Dragonfly, which prefers stony rivers and flies later in the year. The common name refers to the distinctive shape of the abdomen, emphasized by two sets of side flanges on the eighth and ninth segments. It is the only anisopteran dragonfly in Britain that has eyes that are separated.

The Yellow-Legged Dragonfly *Gomphus flavipes* (Charpentier 1825) has been recorded once in Britain, in 1818. The yellow legs have black lines down them and there is a dorsal yellow line along the entire length of the abdomen.

Description
Both the male and female are very similar in appearance; black marked with yellow to pale green, depending on age. The pale green eyes are separated by a black top to the head fringed with green or yellow at the front and rear edges. The light coloration extends from the frons down to the black mouthparts and a black line that runs across the labium. The thorax is mostly lemon yellow to pale green with dark markings, the principal ones being the black bands along the top from the prothorax to the wing-bases and two black bands going down the sides. The legs are

Female

Female

short and black except for the first segment. The male abdomen is black with a series of decreasingly smaller spots and dashes in yellow and green along the top as far as the seventh segment. At this point the abdomen broadens slightly before narrowing again at the last segment. Between the yellow auricles on the second segment are the distinctive black accessory genitalia. The sides of the first three segments and of the eighth and ninth are pale whereas the intervening segments have a yellow spot on each side. The black anal appendages are curved in the manner of a four-pointed grappling iron.

The wings are clear with black veins and large brown to black pterostigmata. The male has angular hindwing-bases, those of the female are rounded. The female abdomen is less club-shaped and has more extensive yellow coloration along the sides. The anal claspers form a pair of short black points.

Larva Average length 27–30 mm.
A distinctive larva in many ways, it has a small heart-shaped head bearing large fat four-segmented antennae. The labium is rectangular and without any large setae or serrated edge to the palps. The abdomen is broad and flat with lateral spines on segments six to nine. Unlike the Aeshnidae the tarsi have two segments on the first two pairs of legs and three on the hind pair.

This hairy larva remains concealed in the mud and silt of sluggish sections of streams and rivers. Emergence takes place on the river-bank. Pollution and the extensive use of river craft are a serious threat to this species.

Behaviour and Habitat
Individuals will mature up to ten kilometres away from a river among the sunny rides and borders of woodland or scrub. Mature males visit the slower millpond-like stretches of a river to set up territories, where they show a distinct preference for sections edged by trees or bushes. The female visits the river only to pair and egg-lay. After pairing among nearby vegetation the female flies unattended to drop the eggs into shallow water where the current is slow. Both sexes spend time sunning themselves on vegetation between bouts of low and feeble (almost damselfly-like) hawking.

Distribution and Time of Appearance
A rare riverine dragonfly confined to the southern half of the country. It may be more widespread than has been recorded because of its short and early season from the end of May to the end of June, possibly extending into July. The rivers Severn, Wye, Thames and Arun each have their own populations where the environmental conditions are right. On the Continent it is widespread from the French Pyrenees east to Russia and south to Italy.

Hairy Dragonfly

Mature male

Average length 55 mm.
Average wingspan 72 mm.

This is one of the hairiest dragonflies; the fine yellow and black down covering the thorax (particularly in the female) can be seen at close range, an obvious adaptation to the cooler weather expected in late spring and early summer. It is the distinctive features of hairy body, early emergence and a long narrow pterostigma which make it unlikely that this species could be confused with the other four Aeshnid Hawkers which are dark brown, spotted with green, yellow and blue.

Description
Both sexes have a yellow head (tinged with pale green in mature males) with various black markings. The male is distinctive in many ways beginning with the pale blue eyes and a thorax which is coloured dark brown on top with two green shoulder stripes (yellow when immature); the sides are also green broken by two thick dark lines. There are yellow spots between the wings. The abdomen is dark brown decorated along the top with sky-blue pear-shaped spots interspersed with small yellow lines, and sides that are pale green or blue on the first few segments. The upper claspers are long and incurved while the lower one is short and cleft. The legs are black. The wings are clear in the male with an angular edge to the hindwing. The veins are black while the costa is yellow and the pterostigma long, thin and light brown.

The female differs in having brown and yellow eyes, yellow shoulder stripes which are only short, and yellow sides to the thorax. Markings along the abdomen are entirely in yellow on a black-brown background. The anal claspers are even longer than in the male. The wings are similar to the male's except for the rounded hindwing and the saffron tinge that extends from the wingbases and along the costal area.

Male

Female

lobes sloping inwards to the midline. The labium is long and waisted. The abdomen has a characteristic dorsal spine on the ninth segment (vestigial on the eighth) in addition to lateral spines on the fifth to ninth segments. The anal appendages are shorter than the ninth and tenth segments combined.

Behaviour and Habitat

This species has suffered as a result of the destruction of its most favoured habitats, the dykes and canals that make up fenland. Where populations still survive, the adults are quite numerous in early summer. Both sexes feed some way from water, flying fast and high over lush herbage in woodland glades. During the heat of the day the males set up regular territories along canals and drainage ditches. Each individual hawks fairly low over the water, weaving in and around emergent reed stems in search of food or a visiting female. Clashes occur when two rivals meet. After pairing, the female will fly off alone to insert eggs with her ovipositor into floating vegetation.

Mature female

Larva Average length 35–40 mm.

In common with other spring species the eggs hatch within three or four weeks of being laid and the larva develops over two years among dead reed stems, sedges, twigs and debris in canals, dykes and ponds.

The smooth larva has a distinctively shaped head bearing two small eyes that have postocular

Distribution and Time of Appearance

Locally common in England and Wales, increasing further south. It occurs in Ireland and was discovered in Scotland a few years ago. Possibly overlooked because of its early season. Its range is across Europe and North Africa.

A short flight period between May and June, exceptionally a week or two longer at either end.

Azure Hawker

Mature male (note extensive sky-blue colouring on abdomen)

Average length 62 mm.
Average wingspan 80 mm.

A rare Hawker in Britain, restricted to high moorland areas in Scotland, an Ice Age relic cut off from other populations in the boreo-alpine regions of Europe. The all blue and brown coloration and smaller size distinguish it from the ubiquitous Common Hawker *A. juncea* with which it might be confused at a distance.

Description
The frons and clypeus are a dirty yellow marked by a black mushroom on top, a black line below the frons and a brown spot on the clypeus. The eyes are a bright blue in contrast to a dark brown thorax with very few light markings. The male has two small stripes on top and two irregular bands on each side; these mature from lilac to sky blue. The abdomen is similarly coloured with very little dark brown patterning. The legs are dark brown. The auricles are pale brown and the leaf-like upper

Mature male

Mature female

Mature female

claspers above a bottle-shaped lower clasper are dark brown. The wing veins and pterostigmata are light brown. The costa is yellow and the clear wings may become tinged with brown on ageing.

The female has grey-brown eyes and a thorax similar to the male's but without the light-coloured shoulder stripes. The top of the abdomen is medium to dark brown marked with a series of light-coloured spots that vary from lavender grey to beige. Some segments may have a pair of small cream triangles.

Larva Average length 35 mm.
The Azure Hawker is particularly well adapted to surviving in a cold climate. The eggs diapause so that the larvae hatch in the following spring and take over two years to mature. They live at the bottom of sphagnum bog pools.

The larva has a typical Aeshnid shape and non-hairy body. The head is slightly rectangular and the labium slightly slimmer than *A. juncea*. There are lateral spines on the seventh to ninth segments (sometimes vestigial on the sixth), the last pair extending by only a third over the tenth segment. The tip of the epiproct is bifid unlike the straight edge of *A. mixta*.

Behaviour and Habitat
This species feeds in birch glades, frequently sunning itself on tree trunks or boulders. During the warmth of midday the males fly low over boggy areas in search of a suitable female. After pairing, the female flies unaccompanied to shallow sphagnum pools where she inserts eggs into exposed patches of peaty mud.

Distribution and Time of Appearance
Found across the Highlands and in Galloway, it is probably under-recorded, although by no means common. Given that the Northern Emerald Dragonfly *Somatochlora arctica* (which shares similar habitat requirements) occurs in southern Eire, it may eventually be recorded there. It has a wide distribution across the Alps, Black Forest, Riesen Gebirge and Scandinavia. It is also found in Siberia and North America.

There is a short flying season in June and July, sometimes extended into August.

Southern Hawker

Mature male (note abdominal blue and green spots)

Mature male

Average length 70 mm.
Average wingspan 100 mm.

On warm twilit evenings in late summer the ghostly rustle of wings may betray the secretive flight of a Southern Hawker searching for gnats. This species is frequently found in inner city parks and suburban gardens: I have even watched one swoop back and forth through open french windows. It is common along woodland paths and at the edges of lakes. Unlike other dragonflies, it will fly close to anyone walking near its beat.

It is distinguished from the Common Hawker *A. juncea*, which is the same size and shape, by not having a yellow costa or two separate pairs of spots on the last two segments. Although size can be deceptive when a dragonfly is moving, the Migrant Hawker *A. mixta* is smaller and patterned differently.

Description

A large Hawker with apple-green, yellow and, in the male, blue markings. The male has a yellow and green head and on top of the frons is a black T attached to a thin line below. The eyes are blue-green and brown. The thorax is dark brown with green spots between the wings as well as two broad shoulder stripes of the same colour. The sides are also green (unlike the Common Hawker *A. juncea*, which is yellow) broken by a thick and a thin brown stripe. The legs are dark brown. The abdomen is brown, marked with bright pairs of coloured spots. On top these markings are green except for the last three segments which consist of two spots followed by two bars, all in sky blue. The small triangles of coloration are in yellow. A series of the spots decorates the sides as well.

The upper claspers are long, pointed, incurved and leaf-like with a yellow line on the inside. The lower clasper is half as long and triangular. The wings are clear except in very old individuals, which acquire a saffron tinge; the veins are black and the pterostigma darkens from red-brown to dark brown.

The female has a yellow head with green eyes, and the light colour of the thorax ages from pale cream to yellow. The abdomen in females and young males is marked in yellow and apple green.

Female

Mature female

The dark brown female claspers are straight and leaf-like. The hindwing in the male is angular, whereas the female has rounder wings.

Larva Average length 38–48 mm.
The eggs overwinter and hatch in spring, when growth is rapid during the warm seasons. This species seems to be showing increased tolerance for overwintering further north before emerging in its second summer.

The larva has seven-segmented antennae typical of the Aeshnidae and a smooth body characteristic of weed dwellers. Note the difference from *Anax*, which shares the same habitat. The labium is long and fairly narrow and the epiproct at the tip of the abdomen is concave unlike other *Aeshnas*. Lateral spines edge the sixth to ninth segments. The mottled granular patterning in browny green is excellent camouflage among the weeds of ponds, lakes and canals.

Behaviour and Habitat
After maturing away from water, in woodland glades and hedgerows, the male will regularly visit a stretch of water for periods of ten to forty minutes at a time. It will fly round the perimeter and make short bursts of hovering. This species operates a form of timeshare whereby a number of males repeatedly visit the same pond or canal at different times of the day. As population density increases, individuals fight more but stay for shorter periods and visit more often. After pairing high up in the trees, the female flies unaccompanied to a mossy bank, submerged vegetation or rotting wood. A series of eggs is hurriedly thrust into the substrate using a curved ovipositor, while the wings keep rustling against the vegetation.

Distribution and Time of Appearance
Primarily a southern species with a preference for neutral to alkaline waters, rare further north, although it has been recorded breeding in Scotland. Its range extends across southern and central Europe and around the Mediterranean to the Middle East.

Seen between July and the end of September.

Brown Hawker

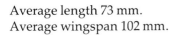
Mature male (note orange wing veins and blue spots)

Mature male

Average length 73 mm.
Average wingspan 102 mm.

The Brown Hawker is one of two large brown dragonflies and the only one with blue markings and brown wing veins. The other species, *A. isosceles*, is now confined to Norfolk and has an earlier flying season. The Brown Hawker is a common late-summer dragonfly frequently encountered flying high over sheltered grassland as well as open water. The ginger-tinted wings are an attractive sight, particularly when they catch the orange light of sunset; this species may stay on the wing until after dusk.

Description
This is a medium brown dragonfly with lemon-yellow and sky-blue markings. The frons is yellow with a brown spot and the eyes of the male are blue. The thorax is brown except for two broad bands of yellow edged in black along the sides and blue and yellow spots on the wingbases. Occasionally the top of the thorax may have two small blue or yellow spots anterior to the wings. The legs are tawny brown. The abdomen is brown, marked with blue spots on the top of segments two and three and along the sides of the other segments, and there may be yellow as well. The auricles are small and brown, and the upper claspers leaf-like

Mature female

Mature female

with a triangular lower appendage. The wings have ginger-brown veins and pterostigmata, and the membranule is small; there is an overall saffron tinge to the wings.

The female is similar to the male in colours and markings. She differs primarily in the eyes, which are browny yellow, and the lack of blue spots on top of the more robust abdomen. The spots along the sides are yellow.

Larva Average length 40–46 mm.
This species lives among the roots and weeds of alkali-rich ponds and lakes. The young larvae have a banded pattern until they reach 30 mm., as a protection from being eaten by older larvae. They eventually emerge from the water two years or more after the eggs were laid. *A. grandis* is typical of the genus, being large, smooth and robust with a slightly rectangular head. The species has lateral spines on the sixth to ninth segments (sometimes vestigial on the fifth), the last one extending halfway down the tenth. The epiproct is bifid like *A. juncea* but the labium is not as broad, though more so than *A. cyanea*.

Behaviour and Habitat
Unlike most other Hawkers, this species will defend a territory away from open water and not visit the breeding sites for as long. While over water it will fly quite high along the outer margins of emergent vegetation and attack intruders that overlap its patch. Common in late summer over ponds, lakes and canals.

The female lays her eggs alone, inserting them into floating vegetation or submerged logs with her strong ovipositor.

Distribution and Time of Appearance
The Brown Hawker is common in eastern and southern England, less so further north and west. It has been recorded in Ireland quite widely, but not in Scotland. Common in northern and central Europe, but not found in the Mediterranean region.

Most frequently seen between July and September, but may occur a couple of weeks either side of these months.

Norfolk Hawker

Immature male

Average length 67 mm.
Average wingspan 93 mm.

The Norfolk Hawker is one of the rarest species in Britain, confined to the remaining dykes around the Norfolk Broads. It can be distinguished from its more common relative, the Brown Hawker *A. grandis*, in numerous ways. At a distance the green eyes, light brown body and clear wings are obvious. Closer inspection of one that has settled reveals the diagnostic yellow isosceles triangle on the abdomen and the large orange membrane of the hindwings. It appears much earlier in the year although there is some overlap at the end of its flight period.

Description

The overall body colour of both sexes is pale brown with green eyes. The frons is ochre yellow topped by a narrow black line. The thorax is light brown, occasionally with pale yellow marks on top and always with two lemon to cream bars on each side. The legs are ochre brown. The abdomen is also a light brown edged in yellow spots. The second segment has a long pointed yellow triangle and there is a dark brown central line running through the eighth and ninth segments. The small auricles are yellow and the claspers thin and leaf-like. The wings are clear (sometimes with a hint of saffron along the forewing) with black veins except for the yellow-brown costa and pterostigma.

Mature female (note yellow triangle on abdomen)

Mature male (note green eyes)

The orange-yellow membranule is characteristic.

The female is very similar in colouring and markings to the male.

Larva Average length 38–44 mm.

The non-diapause eggs hatch after three or four weeks and the larva grows among the weeds and rushes of dykes and Broads for two years. Its preferred habitat is threatened by drainage and by fertilizers which promote excessive algal growth.

The larva is very similar to other Aeshnidae. It has a large rectangular head and a stout body with lateral spines on the sixth to ninth segments, the last one extending just beyond halfway down the tenth segment. The epiproct tip is nearly straight and the cerci are two-thirds the length of the paraprocts, slender and incurved.

Behaviour and Habitat

The restrictive habitat requirements of this species have confined it to the Fenlands in the past and prevented its spreading further. It is now restricted to a few of the less disturbed Broads and nearby unpolluted drainage dykes.

It has been seen flying three to six metres high over reedbeds and around trees in woodland clearings. A regular territory is maintained wherever the species feeds, and a mature male will patrol up and down a stretch of dyke, perching occasionally on reeds. At other times this species will adopt an almost gliding flight and settle frequently on suntraps such as bare bark, farm buildings or hollows in otherwise dense herbage. Pairing takes place low down on reeds or herbage.

The eggs are laid in floating vegetation by the solitary female.

Distribution and Time of Appearance

In Britain this species is restricted to the Norfolk Broads and has probably never been widespread. It is essentially a Mediterranean species with a range extending across central Europe into Russia, Turkestan and North Africa. There are pockets of population further north, as far as southern Sweden.

A short flight period from the middle of June to the end of July, exceptionally seen earlier or later than this.

Common Hawker

Female (note small shoulder stripes and yellow costa)

Mature male (note blue spots on abdomen, no green)

Male

Female

Average length 74 mm.
Average wingspan 95 mm.

A large, brightly coloured Hawker flying over acidic waters or moorland is in all probability a Common Hawker. It is distinguished from its closest relative, the Southern Hawker *A. cyanea*, by its yellow costa, often visible in flight, the greater extent of blue on the male, the greatly reduced yellow shoulder stripes, and the absence of a yellow triangle on the second segment, as well as spots rather than bars of colour on the last three segments. The Azure Hawker *A. caerulea* is a smaller and rarer Hawker found in Scotland with entirely blue body markings in the male. The Migrant Hawker *A. mixta* lacks the yellow costa.

The Sub-Arctic Hawker *Aeshna subarctica* (Walker 1908) is very similar to *A. juncea* and could have been overlooked in Scotland where suitable habitats occur. Overall the light colouring is paler, much reduced, and the bands each side of the thorax are blue to yellow-green at the base. The eyes are grey-green or grey-brown.

Description

The head is yellow to green depending on age, with a dark brown T above a line on the top of the frons. The male has beautiful rich blue eyes. The thorax is dark brown with narrow shoulder stripes in yellow, green or blue; there are two similarly coloured stripes on each side, edged in black. The legs are dark brown to black. The abdomen in the male matures from pale yellow through green to a bright blue on a dark brown background with small yellow paired triangles or dashes on all segments except the last three. The male has a triangular lower clasper, flanked by two leaf-like upper claspers.

The wings have black veins and the characteristic bright yellow costa. The pterostigma darkens from yellow to reddish brown. In old individuals, the wings darken to a browny yellow, more especially in females.

The female is similarly patterned to the male, except that the eyes are green or yellow and brown, the shoulder stripes are almost, or entire-ly, non-existent, and the thoracic markings are green (occasionally blue) on a lighter brown background. The upper claspers are similar to the male's. The female has rounded hindwings, unlike the male.

Larva Average length 40–51 mm.

The eggs diapause over winter and the larva lives for over two years on average, among weeds and submerged shoots in acidic pools, weedy ponds and lakes. A typical weed-loving Aeshnid larva with a five-sided but rectangular-shaped head. Distinguished from relatives by having only a vestigial lateral spine on the sixth segment, the ninth spine extending over a third down the side of the tenth segment. The epiproct is bifid as in *A. grandis* but the labium is broader than either this species or *A. cyanea*.

Behaviour and Habitat

This species is capable of flying in fairly cool summer temperatures as long as it is not raining. A break in the clouds will soon bring individuals from their shelter among heather and bracken. They can then resume their relentless hawking along a coniferous ride, a rocky stream or a moor-land pool. Away from water, they may fly quite high up but males tend to patrol lower down when searching by a pond for a visiting female. After pairing in heather or up in the trees, the female visits a pool or other suitable site to deposit eggs in the stems of submerged vegetation or soft peat.

Distribution and Time of Appearance

A widely distributed species throughout the British Isles with a distinct preference for the north and west, where it can tolerate the cooler temperatures or more acid water. Strong populations exist further east where conditions are favourable. A circumboreal species found in Europe as far south as the Alps and Spain, eastwards in Asia to Mongolia and across North America. More often met with in mountainous regions.

It is most often seen between July and September but warm conditions may extend its appearance a few weeks more.

Migrant Hawker

Mature male

Mature male

Average length 63 mm.
Average wingspan 85 mm.

Although many species of dragonfly are becoming scarce, the Migrant Hawker presents something of a success story. It is a Mediterranean species that has slowly extended its range; at one time it visited Britain as a scarce southern vagrant but now it is an established breeding species as far north as the Midlands. It is the smallest of the three blue, green and yellow *Aeshnas* in Britain as well as possessing the longest claspers. Its brown costa distinguishes it from the Common Hawker *A. juncea*, whose costa is yellow.

The Southern Migrant Hawker *Aeshna affinis* (van der Linden 1820) is a migratory hawker similar to *A. mixta* that has been recorded in Britain. The sides of the thorax are entirely blue and green except for thin black lines delineating the sutures.

Description
The frons and clypeus of the male are greenish yellow with a black T on top and blue compound eyes. Characteristically the male has very faint pale yellow antehumeral stripes on its brown thorax although there are two yellow-green bands on each side. The legs are dark brown to black. All the large spots on a mature male abdomen are sky blue (lilac grey in immatures) with distinctive cream markings on the second and third segments. The tawny background colour becomes progressively darker brown with age. The male auricles are inconspicuous but the claspers are as long as the ninth and tenth segments combined.

The female differs in coloration, although the patterning is similar. The eyes are green and the abdominal spots are a dull green when mature. The clear wings have yellow-brown pterostigmata.

Larva Average length 30–38 mm.
The eggs diapause over the winter and the larva grows rapidly in the space of two to five months to emerge in late summer. It seems that the inability

Aeshna mixta (LATRIELLE 1805)

Mature female (note long anal appendages)

Immature female, abdominal spots lilac grey, one appendage is damaged

of the larva to tolerate low temperatures or to overwinter is the reason for this species' absence from the north of England and Scotland.

The head is five-sided with large eyes and a long labium that is narrow at the base. The legs are long and slender while the abdomen is short and stout. Note the long pointed anal appendages, and the long lateral spines on segment nine that nearly reach the end of segment ten. It is found in the weeds of lakes and ponds and is dark greyish brown in colour.

Behaviour and Habitat

Males may be seen hawking low over the water a few metres from the margin of lakes, ponds and canals. They are very wary and tend to move along the shoreline when approached. At other times both sexes may be seen flying four or more metres up in woodland clearings and hedgerows, sometimes in fair numbers but without any sign of aggression or sexual behaviour. Spectacular mass migrations have been recorded involving millions of dragonflies moving across Europe from the south. Pairing takes place among vegetation bordering a stretch of water. The female lays her eggs alone by inserting them into the stems and leaves of rushes, usually some way above the water level. Such behaviour is characteristic of a late-summer species, presumably in anticipation of rising water levels in the autumn.

Distribution and Time of Appearance

A frequent migrant from southern Europe but a locally common breeding species in south Wales and England up to the Midlands, not found in Scotland and Ireland. On the Continent its range extends from Spain to Turkey and south Russia, taking in Algeria and the Middle East, and reaching further eastwards to Tibet.

It is most often seen in August and September although it may be encountered a month earlier and also well into November if warm weather permits.

Emperor Dragonfly

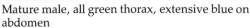
Mature male, all green thorax, extensive blue on abdomen

Mature male

Average length 78 mm.
Average wingspan 106 mm.

The Emperor is our largest species of dragonfly by virtue of its broad wings and long robust body. (The female Golden-Ringed Dragonfly *Cordulegaster boltonii* is slightly longer but slimmer.) The male is an impressive sight in the heat of summer, an aggressive defender of large ponds and lakes, tirelessly hawking far from the shore, only settling to devour a particularly large victim or to wait for the sun to reappear. The enamel-blue abdomen broken by a dark central line with crossbars distinguishes it from the male *Aeshnas* which have blue spots on a dark background.

The Saddle-Back Dragonfly *Hemianax ephippiger* (Burmeister 1839) is an African migrant that has reached the shores of England and Eire a few times. The overall colour is light brown and yellow with a distinctive saddle shape on the second abdominal segment. This is blue in the male but rather dull in the female.

Description

Both sexes are originally pale green with brown markings but as the colour matures the male acquires a blue abdomen, as do some very old females. The male has a grass-green head with large blue eyes. There may be some yellow on the frons and clypeus below a horizontal blue line. The thorax is apple green, turning bluish in old males. The legs are dark brown, yellowish near the base. The abdomen is rich blue with a black fishbone pattern down the centre. The claspers are broad, leaf-like and hairy above a short square lower appendage. The wings, which are black veined with a yellow costa, become tinted yellow-brown on ageing. Both sexes have rounded hind-wings and a pterostigma that may be any shade of brown.

The female is predominantly green with similar markings to the male. The last few segments tend to be browny-coloured and the claspers are more delicate than the male's.

Mature female

Mature female

Larva Average length 45–56 mm.

The eggs hatch a few weeks after being laid and the larva grows rapidly during the summer. By the autumn of the following year it enters the final instar. The winter diapause or resting phase allows some individuals to catch up so that a synchronized emergence is possible in early summer.

The larva has an almost round, flattened head with a straight rear edge to its large eyes. The body is long and robust, fairly glabrous with lateral spines on the seventh to ninth segments. The banded pattern of larvae under 20 mm. is thought to be a protective sign to prevent larger conspecifics eating first-year larvae.

The Emperor larva hunts voraciously among the weeds of ponds, lakes and canals, and is capable of tackling prey larger than itself, such as small fish.

Behaviour and Habitat

During the warmth of midday mature males will set up territories over weedy ponds and lakes, flying fast between two and six metres above the surface. One male may occupy a small pond, vigorously fending off intruders and attacking other species that fly too close. They rarely rest but when they do on hot afternoons it is usually on the edge of reedbeds or high up in the tree canopy.

After pairing (often high up on a tree) the female inserts her eggs into floating vegetation such as *Potamogeton*. To avoid being harassed by a territorial male, she keeps low over the vegetation and bends her abdomen down into a right angle as a signal that she does not want to mate.

Distribution and Time of Appearance

A southern species most common in areas below a line from Fishguard to the Wash. Fairly common where the habitat is right. It is widespread across Europe, North Africa, the Middle East and north-west India. A subspecies extends its range through the tropics to South Africa.

An early-summer species most common in June and July but sometimes lasting into August, exceptionally a couple of weeks outside this period. Individuals may live over two months although the average is four weeks.

Golden-Ringed Dragonfly

Mature male, eyes just meet

Average length: male 74 mm., female 84 mm. Average wingspan 101 mm.

The Golden-Ringed Dragonfly is a distinctively large black dragonfly with lemon-yellow bands and markings. The female has a pronounced ovipositor making it our longest species and possibly the origin of the myth that dragonflies can sting like giant wasps. The only species it might be confused with is the Club-Tailed Dragonfly *Gomphus vulgatissimus*, but the latter is decidedly smaller and does not have a banded pattern.

Description

Both sexes have apple-green eyes and identical markings in black and yellow on the rest of the body. The head is yellow with a black area on top between the eyes and dark lines across the clypeus and labrum; the mouthparts are also black. The prothorax has a yellow edge to it, while the thorax is marked on top by two yellow bands and on each side by three yellow stripes. There are two yellow spots between the wingbases. Downy yellow hair covers the head and thorax. The legs are black with a yellow base.

Mature female

Female (note long ovipositor extending beyond tip of abdomen)

The abdomen is very slightly club-shaped and banded by a series of lemon-yellow lines on a matt black background. The male auricles are small and yellow, while the claspers are black; the upper pair curve outwards to small points whereas the lower set are slightly shorter and blunt-ended.

The female has small indistinct appendages but a very prominent black pointed ovipositor, which extends some way beyond the end of the abdomen. The wings are clear until late maturity when they acquire a browny yellow cast. In males the hindwing is angular whereas in the females it is rounded. The veins are black and dense towards the wingtips, and the costa is yellow. The pterostigma turns from light brown to black with maturity.

Larva Average length 35–42 mm.
The distinctly hairy larva remains buried, with only its head and tip of the abdomen exposed, in the mud of streams for over two years before emerging at night, crawling some distance, perhaps climbing a tree, and transforming itself into a winged imago.

The head is distinctively shaped, short and broad with small protruding eyes. The labium is spoon-shaped and the palps have irregular, deeply serrated edges. The body is large and hairy with lateral spines on the eighth and ninth segments.

Behaviour and Habitat
Both sexes roam over patches of vegetation or woodland when feeding, but during the middle of the day they make for suitable rendezvous sites such as mountain or heathland streams. The males do not have exclusive territories but each one adopts several hundred metres of stream as a home range. They fly moderately fast and straight about ten to thirty centimetres above the water, occasionally turning for a short distance before proceeding further along the beat. Males only fight one another if they meet head-on. A female making a short visit is chased and seized from above by the male. The pair then rest on vegetation away from the river. After copulation the female egg-lays alone using her long ovipositor to thrust eggs into shallow mud or silt. This is accomplished by hovering and bobbing up and down over the surface.

Distribution and Time of Appearance
Common in western regions of Britain, with populations further eastwards in areas of acidic heathland. Found right across Europe to northern India. It is seen on the wing from June to September, more often met in July and August.

Downy Emerald

Mature male

Average length 48 mm.
Average wingspan 68 mm.

The Downy Emerald is the most widespread metallic Hawker dragonfly, not easily distinguished at a distance from the other two Emeralds. It is the least metallic of the three, the green is rather bronze looking and in flight the dragonfly may look black. It is distinctive in other ways: the yellow markings on the head occur only on the labium and across the labrum, and the anal claspers are relatively short.

The Orange-Spotted Emerald *Oxygastra curtisii* (Dale 1834) became extinct from its last known site in Hampshire as a result of habitat destruction. The distinguishing feature is a series of yellow spots along the top of its metallic green abdomen.

Description

Both sexes are similar. The eyes are a beautiful bright green colour. The rest of the head is bronze-green like polished metal, with a bright yellow bar on the labrum and a yellow labium. The bronze-green thorax has a yellow covering of downy hair, which extends over the rest of the body. The legs are dark brown to black. The abdomen is dark bronze-green and in the male club-shaped with a reddish tinge to the later segments. There is a thin yellow line between the second and third segments and the same colour along the side of these two segments. The male auricles are small and black and the upper claspers curve outwards slightly. The lower appendage is curved upwards, deeply cleft and has two points on the end.

The wings are clear with a saffron area at the base, but in mature females the whole of the wings may be tinged. The pterostigma is small and dark.

The female has a more cylindrical abdomen and a pair of straight pointed appendages, and a deeply cleft vulvar scale below segment eight.

Male   Mature female

Larva Average length 24 mm.

The eggs are laid as a gelatinous mass and hatch in about two weeks. The larva takes over two years to mature. It is a flat, stumpy-looking larva that lies half submerged among vegetable detritus of well-reeded ponds and lakes. It is sparsely covered in short bristles and coloured sepia with yellowy green marks. It has prominent mid-dorsal spines from the fourth to the ninth segments (small and vestigial on the last). The cerci are more than half the length of the paraprocts. The margin of the labial palp has deep crenations but there are no outer spines on the prementum.

Behaviour and Habitat

The male flies at great speed over floating vegetation on sheltered ponds, lakes and canals. Part of the regular beat may involve short bursts of hovering nearer the shore between emergent vegetation. The female is more often seen hawking along woodland glades. After pairing up in the trees, the female flies unaccompanied to lay her eggs in shady patches of shallow water, dipping the tip of her abdomen into the water to wash off the gelatinous eggs. In common with the other Emeralds, this species may visit the rendezvous site until late evening.

Female

Distribution and Time of Appearance

Most common in the south of England but it has been recorded in most regions including Scotland and southern Eire. Its range extends across north and central Europe as far as the Alps and Siberia.

The flight period is from the middle of May to the end of July.

Northern Emerald

Mature male (note caliper-like claspers)

Average length 50 mm.
Average wingspan 68 mm.

This is a fast-flying dark dragonfly with emerald eyes, and a rare sight even in its favoured habitat of sphagnum pools among the Caledonian pine forests of Scotland and the peat bogs of County Kerry. It could easily be mistaken for the other two Emeralds in flight. Characteristically the female has long anal appendages and a blunt vulvar scale; the male has appendages shaped like an earwig's tail. The yellow spot on each side of the clypeus is diagnostic.

The only record for the Alpine Emerald *Somatochlora alpestris* (Selys 1840) is probably a mistake; the nearest Continental populations are in Norway. It is the same size as *S. arctica*, but the male claspers are like those of *S. metallica*, and in both sexes the yellow markings on the head are different from either of the other species. Segments one to three have a thin yellow ring round them and there is a dull yellow spot beneath segment three.

Description

Both sexes are similar although the male has a waisted abdomen in contrast to the stouter female. The eyes and head are bronze-green except for chrome-yellow mouthparts and a spot on each side of the clypeus. The thorax is a shiny metallic green with hints of red, covered in fine yellow hair. The dark abdomen reflects metallic green in certain lights; in the male the first two segments are marked with yellow along the sides and on the small auricles underneath. The anal appendages in the male are caliper-shaped, each one like an inward-pointing hook. The shorter lower appendage forms an upwardly curving tongue shape. The wings are tinged saffron, more so near the base, and the pterostigma is reddish brown.

The female differs in having two dull yellow spots on the third segment and light rings around the first two joints. Overall the abdomen is much more robust-looking, and protruding below the eighth segment is a rather blunt vulvar scale. The female's appendages are cylindrical and almost straight.

Male

Female

Mature female (note yellow spots on abdomen)

Larva Average length 20 mm.
The larvae have been found among the mud and rotting sphagnum of runnels and seepages sheltered by birch and pine. The dorsal surface is covered in spiny hairs but there are no mid-dorsal or lateral spines. The abdomen is short and blunt. Like the other Emeralds, the cerci are over half as long as the paraprocts. The triangular spoon-shaped labium has crenellated labial palps.

After developing for at least two years, the larva will emerge and transform into an adult imago on rushes just above the sphagnum pool.

Behaviour and Habitat
Males will patrol and defend territories over sheltered peaty pools filled with sphagnum moss. They fly fast at a height of three metres or more but may check the margins of the pool by flying low and hovering frequently. The female will visit these small pools from nearby pine and birch woods and after pairing she will oviposit alone. Shallow patches of open water among the sphagnum or patches of mud are sought out as the female hovers, dipping the tip of her abdomen just below the surface.

Distribution and Time of Appearance
The Northern Emerald has been recorded in the Highlands of Scotland and in County Kerry in Ireland. It is a boreo-alpine species found across Scandinavia and the U.S.S.R. Its alpine range extends to France in the west and to the Caucasus in the east.

The fairly short flight period is from the end of June to the beginning of August.

Brilliant Emerald

Mature male

Male

Average length 53 mm.
Average wingspan 78 mm.

The most colourful and metallic of the three Emeralds and particularly beautiful when the light catches its large, almost glowing, jewelled eyes. It can be distinguished from its relatives only by close examination although the female has entirely saffron-brown tinted wings. One unique feature is the bright yellow U-shape across the frons, another is the characteristically straight but thorny-looking male claspers, and a third is the long pointed vulvar scale of the female.

Description

Both sexes are almost entirely metallic green. The eyes are a bright emerald set behind a bronze-green face. There is a chrome-yellow labium and bar across the labrum as well as a distinctive broad U-shape of the same colour on the frons. The shiny green thorax has a fine covering of yellow hair. The legs are black. The abdomen is dark, highlighted in metallic green, turning red towards the tip in the male. Both sexes have two small yellow spots on top of the second segment and a yellow band encircling the joint. There are larger spots of the same colour on the side of the second

Mature female

Female (note pickaxe-like vulvar scale)

and third segments. The male has small black auricles but quite prominent accessory genitalia. The upper claspers are straight and ridged on the outer edge in the male; the lower appendage is triangular and slightly hollowed.

The wings are suffused with saffron, more at the base and in mature females. The pterostigma is red-brown.

The female has two long straight appendages and a spur-like vulvar scale held at right angles to the underside of the eighth segment. Her abdomen is not waisted like the male's.

Larva Average length 25 mm.
This species is very similar to *Cordulia aenea* in having a dorsal surface only sparsely covered in hairs, and hook-like dorsal spines on segments four to nine. The abdomen is broad at the base but less truncated than the other species. Also there are spines on the outer margin of the prementum. It is sepia with a lighter coloured pattern on the abdomen and the legs are long and hairy. It lives among the mud and leaves of ponds, lakes and canals.

Behaviour and Habitat
The preferred habitat is wooded lakes and large ponds, well stocked with weeds. Males will set up regular beats along the shoreline, hovering every so often as they investigate gaps in the emergent vegetation. The abdomen is held slightly above horizontal like the other Emeralds. The female roams fairly high up along woodland rides and margins without a regular beat. Unaccompanied she will fly to patches of mud or shallow water among rushes and mosses to egg-lay. Typically, the female hovers over a suitable surface using her pointed vulvar scale as a pickaxe to bury the eggs. The rustle of wings on emergent vegetation as she searches for a suitable site is often a good give-away to her presence.

Distribution and Time of Appearance
There are two populations, one in the lochs and bogs of the Highlands of Scotland and the other in the sandy ponds and lakes of southern England. There is no obvious explanation as to why it has not spread further. It is found across northern Europe as far south as France and Italy and extending across to Turkey and beyond to Siberia in the east.

On the wing from June to August.

Black-Tailed Skimmer

Mature male (note yellow costa)

Average length 50 mm.
Average wingspan 77 mm.

The increase in gravel pits during the past thirty years as a result of demand for new buildings and roads has benefited the Black-Tailed Skimmer. The powder-blue male likes to sun itself on exposed gravel, between short bursts of fast low flying over open water in defence of territory or searching for food. It is possibly the most common anisopteran dragonfly in the south and east of England.

Both sexes might be confused with the Keeled Skimmer, *O. coerulescens*, and the blue *Libellulas*. The latter species have dark brown wingbases and the Keeled Skimmer is smaller with a pale pterostigma. The mature male Black-Tailed Skimmer is distinguished by its lack of shoulder stripes and by a blue abdomen edged in orange lines and with a black tip. Young males and the females have a parallel set of black lines down the abdomen.

Description
The male has a grey-brown head and green-blue eyes. The thorax is brown, marked with black lines on the top and sides. The legs mature from light brown to black. The abdomen in a mature male is pale blue edged with long orange spots as far as the seventh segment and then black to the tip. In this and other powder-blue species the female's legs rest on the abdomen during copulation and sometimes remove lines of blue colouring. The claspers are black and pointed, the shorter lower appendage curving upwards slightly. The clear wings are edged by a chrome-yellow costa and a dark pterostigma.

The immature male and the female are similar in colour and pattern. The head, thorax and abdomen are yellow maturing through ochre to grey with a thick black line almost at the edge of each abdominal segment. A very old female will sometimes have a powder-blue abdomen.

Male

Old female

Immature female

Larva Average length 23–25·5 mm.

The dark brown hairy larva inhabits the mud and debris of ponds, lakes and gravel pits for over two years. The head is oblong with small prominent eyes, and a broad triangular labium. The triangular labial palps have seven setae (distinguishing the larva from *O. coerulescens*, which has five). The stout legs barely extend beyond the egg-shaped, but slightly tapered, abdomen. The mid-dorsal spines are only on the third to sixth segments and the short lateral spines on the eighth and ninth are not very prominent.

Behaviour and Habitat

The typical habitat for this species is shallow ponds, lakes and gravel pits, even brackish water on occasions. Males set up territories along the shore from ten to fifty metres long and patrol them at great speed, frequently returning to a favoured patch of bare ground or a prominent stick (depending on how hot it is) to sunbathe with wings held down and forwards. Females remain concealed in nearby grassland or reedbeds and only visit open water to pair and egg-lay. After pairing for about five minutes the female slaps the tip of her abdomen into open water to wash off the eggs. Sometimes the male will remain in the vicinity to guard her.

Distribution and Time of Appearance

A very common dragonfly below the Wash-Severn line with scattered records further north, and in Wales and Ireland. Worldwide its range extends from Scandinavia to North Africa and eastwards across to central Asia, in a rather scattered distribution.

On the wing in June and July.

Keeled Skimmer

Mature male (note black marks where blue pruinescence has been rubbed off by female's legs during mating)

Average length 42 mm.
Average wingspan 60 mm.

The name Skimmer comes from the very fast low-level flying this species and its relative, the Black-Tailed Skimmer, perform over low vegetation and open water. The Black-Tailed Skimmer can be distinguished by its greater size and lack of shoulder stripes along with distinctive abdominal patterns and a dark pterostigma. The mature Keeled Skimmer has an entirely blue abdomen, the female has no dark markings. The pale thoracic stripes (which fade with age), median black line and tinted costa should distinguish the female from the *Sympetrum* species.

The Scarlet Dragonfly *Crocothemis erythraea* (Brulle 1832) is a migrant from southern Europe that has been recorded in the Channel Isles. Both sexes are shaped like an *Orthetrum* but the hind-wing-bases are bright saffron or orange. The male is bright red and the female is ochre and brown tinted with olive green. The eyes are blue underneath.

Description
The mature male has a grey frons and clypeus in front of smoky blue eyes. The thorax is brown decorated with two cream dorsal stripes and yellowish bands on the sides, all of which darken with age to a dull grey-blue colour. The legs are dark brown to black. The abdomen is entirely pale powder blue terminated by sharply pointed upper claspers and a broader upturned lower appendage. The wings in mature males are clear with a light-coloured pterostigma varying from straw to red-brown.

Orthetrum coerulescens (FABRICIUS 1798)

Immature male

Female (note pale yellow pterostigma)

Male

The immature male resembles the female, which has an ochre-coloured head with darker brownish eyes and a similarly coloured thorax marked with two cream dorsal stripes and cream sides smudged with brown. The abdomen is yellow-brown, slim and slightly keeled along the top, emphasized by the thin dark medial line. The claspers are short and pointed. The legs are yellow-brown and the wings are tinted saffron along the costa; this tint extends over the entire wing in many individuals.

Larva Average length 17–23 mm.

The hairy, bee-shaped larva has a rectangular head with small prominent eyes and a broad short labium bearing three to five labial setae. The stout legs barely extend beyond the abdomen, which has mid-dorsal spines on the fourth to seventh segments and a smooth raised mid-dorsal area on the eighth and ninth, which bear short lateral spines. The larva lives at the bottom of streams and weedy pools, in acid bogs and marshes, for over two years before emergence.

Behaviour and Habitat

The male patrols up and down a favoured stream, or circles and zigzags across a boggy pool or patch of wet marshland during the middle of the day, stopping frequently at a favoured perch. Intruding males are approached by a direct rapid flight from below or to the side. Should a female visit the rendezvous area she is rapidly approached from above, grasped by the back of the head and taken in tandem to the centre of the territory. Copulation most often occurs in the afternoon and may last from a few seconds to nearly half an hour. The pair fly in tandem or with the male in close pursuit to open water, where the female oviposits by striking the surface with the tip of her abdomen. The male hovers nearby to fend off potential rivals. Those males that are unable to defend a territory wander in search of new sites or attempt to take over occupied ones.

The favoured habitat is acid bogs, marshes and moorland with running water or peaty ditches and sphagnum pools.

Distribution and Time of Appearance

Widely recorded from suitable habitats across the British Isles, the Keeled Skimmer is also found in Europe from Fennoscandia to the Mediterranean countries and across to Russia in the east.

The flight period extends from the end of May to September, most common from the end of June to August.

Broad-Bodied Chaser

Mature male

Average length 44 mm.
Average wingspan 76 mm.

The Broad-Bodied Chaser is a fast-flying inhabitant of well-vegetated ponds and lakes. It is a victim of the neglect and drainage of many farm ponds. Essentially it is a southern species that has migrated further north and established colonies beyond its preferred range for a time. The broad flattened body with dark wingbases but no wing spots is a distinctive feature of this species. The male has an attractive powder-blue abdomen bordered by yellow spots, and light-coloured shoulder stripes. The female does not have any dark abdominal markings to confuse it with the other *Libellulas* or the Black-Tailed Skimmer *Orthetrum cancellatum*. The pterostigma is longer and narrower than in the Scarce Chaser *L. fulva*.

Description

The male looks like the female until it acquires mature colours. The frons is brown turning a bluish colour with age in the male. The eyes and thorax are dark brown except for a pair of two-tone grey-blue and yellow shoulder stripes and a black line across the top of the sides. The legs are dark brown with lighter bases. The abdomen has a light blue pruinescence bordered by yellow spots. The claspers are short and blunt in the upper pair, triangular and curved upwards in the lower one. The wings are clear, each one having a basal patch of dark brown marked by a lighter centre and yellow vein; note the light membranule. The pterostigma is brown to black.

The female has a similar head and thorax coloration except that the thorax is usually lighter. The abdomen is broader, light brown and edged with

Mature male

Mature female

Mature female

yellow spots. The female anal appendages are short and inconspicuous.

Larva Average length 22·5–25 mm.
The eggs hatch after two to four weeks and maturation usually takes over two years. A very tubby-looking hairy larva, flattened, and a sepia brown mottled colour. The stout legs barely go beyond the tip of the abdomen. The head is rectangular with prominent eyes and a broad spoon-shaped labium. There are obtuse, mid-dorsal spines on segments four to eight (sometimes a vestige on three) and short lateral spines on segments eight to nine. Its structure makes the larva ideally suited to a life hidden among the rotting debris and leaves of pools, ponds and lakes.

Behaviour and Habitat
The male is an aggressive territorial defender during midday and early afternoon over and around well-vegetated ponds, ditches and lakes. It has also been seen over brackish marshes. Fast direct flights from an exposed perch are made in search of intruders or visiting females. Pairing is brief, after which the female slaps the tip of her broad abdomen into open water; sometimes the male hovers nearby. At other times the female settles among neighbouring vegetation.

Distribution and Time of Appearance
This is essentially a southern and Midlands species, most common below the Mersey–Wash line. It has a tendency to migrate, sometimes establishing colonies further north. It has been recorded across Wales but not in Scotland or Ireland. The world range extends across all of Europe and into Asia Minor and Syria.

An early-summer species, it may be found on the wing from the beginning of May in good years to mid August. It is most common in June and July.

Scarce Chaser

Mature male (note black tip and dark wing bases)

Male sunning itself, abdomen raised so as to present less body area to the sun

Average length 44 mm.
Average wingspan 74 mm.

Possibly the most attractive and certainly the rarest Chaser, with a restricted southern distribution that has diminished considerably through lack of habitat. The male is a delicate powder blue, tipped with black, while the female is an even more striking tan-orange broken by a black line. Both sexes have blue eyes. The wing patches at the base distinguish it from the Black-Tailed Skimmer *Orthetrum cancellatum* and the absence of wing spots distinguishes it from the Four-Spotted Chaser *L. quadrimaculata*. The only other confusion is likely to be with the Broad-Bodied Chaser *L. depressa* but here the male has shoulder stripes and a blue abdomen flanked by yellow spots, while the female lacks the dark central line of the Scarce Chaser *L. fulva*.

Description

The frons matures from yellow-brown to dark blue-black in the male and the eyes are grey-blue turning green underneath. The entire thorax is dark brown and hairy, the legs are similarly coloured but with a tan-coloured base. The abdomen becomes covered in a pale blue pruinescence except for the first segment and the last three segments, which remain black. The male upper appendages are nearly as long as the last two segments, the lower one forms a long triangle between. The wings are clear except for brown-black wingbases (sometimes absent in the forewings) and streaks of yellow radiating along the wings just behind the costa. The pterostigma is black.

The females and immature males possess a light brown frons, dark thorax above and a most attractive orange-tan abdomen with a black central line

Mature female

Old female beginning to acquire male pruinescence

beginning on the fourth segment. In addition, the female has a dark patch at the tip of each wing, a feature sometimes occurring in the male. The female anal appendages are slightly shorter.

Larva Average length 22–25 mm.
The eggs hatch a few days after being laid, early in the year, and the larva may take over two years before emerging. It lives hidden among the mud and detritus of dykes, streams and ponds, and is hairy and stumpy-looking, with a ridged abdomen topped by large recurved spines on segments four to nine (one more than the other *Libellulas*). The broad abdomen also has short lateral spines on segments eight and nine. The rather small head possesses a spoon-shaped labium bearing triangular palps, with a maximum of only five bristles each, a diagnostic feature.

Behaviour and Habitat
This species has a preference for muddy lowland streams and rivers bordered by drainage dykes. It may also colonize nearby ponds and pools. Males will set up territories along the water margins and aggressively patrol them from suitable exposed perches. Clashes frequently occur between them. Pairing takes longer than in other *Libellulas* and the pair actually settle on vegetation for a short while. The female lays her eggs hovering over the water and slapping the tip of her abdomen on to the surface. The male remains in attendance to chase off intruding competitors.

Distribution and Time of Appearance
A very rare and local dragonfly with colonies in the south and east of England. Land drainage and reclamation schemes have deprived this species of some of its best habitats in the Fens and Norfolk Broads. A wide but local distribution in Europe from Scandinavia to the Mediterranean and east to Russia.

One of the earliest dragonflies to appear, sometimes recorded at the end of May. It has a short flying season and is most common in June and at the beginning of July.

Four-Spotted Chaser

Mature male

Average length 43 mm.
Average wingspan 75 mm.

A tawny to grey-brown dragonfly with coloured wingbases, this species is distinguished from the Black-Tailed Skimmer *Orthetrum cancellatum* and the other *Libellulas* by four dark wing spots, one at each node. The males may be seen hovering and swooping over a variety of wetland habitats as they defend their territories by aggressive dog-fighting. The Four-Spot has a reputation for spectacular migrations over Europe. Eyewitness accounts put estimates of numbers into billions when great clouds of them darken the sky like a locust plague. High pressure, light winds and parasitic irritation trigger off westward migrations after a ten-year population explosion cycle.

The Globe Skimmer *Pantala flavescens* (Fabricius 1798) is a worldwide migrant that sometimes reaches Europe from tropical Africa. It is about the same length as *L. quadrimaculata* with deep hindwings that reach almost halfway down the abdomen. Overall ochre to red-brown with a tapered abdomen and dark marks on the ninth and tenth segments.

Description
The sexes are very similar. The frons and clypeus area is whitish yellow, and there are yellow and black markings on the labrum, the labium and behind the rim of the brown eyes. The thorax is brown, marked on the side by two irregular black lines and bright yellow patches in younger individuals. The legs are black. The brown tapered abdomen has the first and seventh to tenth segments black; there are yellow spots down each

Mature male

Old female (note the reduction in yellow colouring)

side as well. The male upper claspers are long, black and slightly curved outwards, the lower one forms a long triangle. The body is covered in fine downy yellow hair. With ageing, individuals turn darker to an oily grey-brown. The wingbases are dark brown to black, streaked above and some way along the costa in saffron. Each node has a characteristic brown spot of varying size, and the pterostigma can be brown to black. There is a form *praenubila* Newman which has an additional brown smudge spot on the tip of each wing. In certain lights the wings look grey-blue.

Females have only two upper anal appendages, otherwise they are coloured and patterned similarly to the male.

Larva Average length 22–26 mm.
The eggs hatch after a few weeks and the larvae develop for over two years among the mud and debris of ponds, lakes, bog pools, canals and even slow-moving streams and brackish water. Exuviae may be found clinging to upright vegetation not far from the water's edge in early summer. The larva is stubby and arched by mid-dorsal spines on segments four to eight. It is a uniform sepia colour beneath the muddy bristles and there are short lateral spines on the eighth and ninth segments. The eyes protrude laterally and the labium extends beyond the front of the head, more so than in *L. depressa*. The seventh segment on the antenna is longer than the sixth. The labium is broad and spoon-shaped.

Behaviour and Habitat
Once the sun is out males will parcel up the surface of a pond or boggy area and aggressively defend their own patch throughout the middle of the day and into late afternoon.

Each individual hovers and dashes about at great speed, using a direct flight, a metre or so above the water. Fast deviations may be made to attack an intruding male, resulting in a noisy clash of wings. A prominent twig or a reed is used as a perch to which the male regularly but briefly returns. Pairing lasts only a matter of seconds and is carried out in flight over water. The female then lays her eggs by hovering and dipping the tip of her abdomen up and down into water. She is frequently pestered by males unless her partner fends them off. Afterwards the female flies to her usual haunts well away from water.

This species may be seen in a variety of habitats including almost any open water, marshes, woodland glades, moorland, town gardens and brackish coastal areas.

Distribution and Time of Appearance
A circumboreal species whose range extends beyond the British Isles across Europe, from Scandinavia to the Mediterranean, to Russia, China, Japan and North America.

Most often seen in June and July but it may also be seen in late May to September, depending on the weather and migratory movements from the Continent.

Black Darter

Mature male

Mature male

Average length 32 mm.
Average wingspan 46 mm.

The Black Darter is a common sight hovering over acidic wetlands and the surrounding moor or heathland in summer. It shares similar habitats with the White-Faced Dragonfly *Leucorrhinia dubia* but is usually on the wing later in the year. The latter species has a distinctive white face and dark wingbases, and the male has crimson body markings.

Description
Males mature from colouring very similar to the female, to an almost entirely black head, thorax and abdomen, the only exceptions being some lemon yellow on the frons and dark brown eyes. The male has a slightly waisted abdomen at the beginning of segment three, and two short pointed upper claspers and a small triangular lower one. The wings of the male are entirely clear with a pterostigma which matures from yellow to black.

Females are primarily black and lemon, ageing to ochre yellow, and young males look very simi-

lar to this before they darken in sexual maturity. The frons and clypeus are yellow topped by a black line and the eyes are red-brown above, greenish below. There is a black triangle on top of the thorax with the apex pointing towards the yellow wing joints. On the side of the thorax there is a yellow spot in front of two broad yellow bands, separated by a black bar marked by three small spots of yellow. The abdomen is lemon to ochre with black along the sides and on most of segments nine and ten. The black anal appendages are short and pointed. The female has a touch of deep saffron on each wingbase.

Larva Average length 14–16 mm.
In Britain the eggs diapause and the larva grows within a year to maturity. A typical long-legged *Sympetrum* larva with a rounded posterior margin to the head, a triangular labium, and mid-dorsal spines on segments five to seven. The lateral spines on segments eight and nine are short. The overall appearance is rather smooth with a few bristles on the legs. It is found in acidic weedy pools and ponds.

Nearly mature female (note black triangle on top of thorax)

Old female

Female

Behaviour and Habitat

The males fly one or two metres above the emergent vegetation of boggy ponds in marshy or peaty areas. Between hovering and darting about they repeatedly land on a favourite perch, or settle down among the rushes should the sun go in. If they perch on bleached pine they are particularly well camouflaged. Females tend to remain away from water, keeping low down among grasses or heather. As soon as one of them flies to an exposed section of water she is approached by a male, they pair up and then retire to nearby vegetation to mate. Egg-laying is performed by the female slapping the surface of the water with the tip of her abdomen while hovering. The male may remain in attendance until she disappears into the vegetation.

This species has been observed over brackish water as well as in its more usual acid peat habitat.

Distribution and Time of Appearance

A circumboreal species spreading in a band from just below the Arctic Circle to the Alps. Apart from its widespread distribution in the British Isles it is found on the Continent, and across the U.S.S.R. to China and Japan. It also occurs in northern Canada and British Columbia.

Most common in August and September, exceptionally it is seen at the end of June through to November.

Yellow-Winged Darter

Mature male

Average length 34 mm.
Average wingspan 55 mm.

The Yellow-Winged Darter is an infrequent visitor to the shores of Britain, sometimes arriving in the company of Clouded Yellow butterflies. It is a distinctive dragonfly because of the large orange-yellow wing patches in both sexes, which flash like stained glass in bright sunlight.

Description

The eyes are brick red above and brown below in mature males. The red frons has a black line extending across the vertex and partway down the side of the eyes. The thorax is red above and yellow to red on the sides, broken by three thin black lines. The legs are black, and yellow or red. The abdomen is scarlet with a black line across the second segment, a black streak along the top of the

Mature male

Mature female

Mature female

Larva Average length 16·5 mm.
A similar larva to the Black Darter *S. danae*; see the key to determine differences in the labial palp setae. Records of larvae or exuviae would be an obvious confirmation of a breeding site. Found in boggy pools and weedy ponds on the Continent.

Behaviour and Habitat

This species has an irregular twisting flight over rushes and sedges just beyond the margins of ponds and lakes. After a short hover an individual will drop down into a sheltered pocket within the emergent vegetation. A female that moves into the rendezvous site will be approached by one of the males and taken into the sedges for mating. The pair subsequently fly off in tandem to oviposit. The male may break off and leave the hovering female to dip her abdomen up and down into shallow, almost muddy water. There seems to be a preference for slightly acidic water with plenty of emergent vegetation.

Distribution and Time of Appearance

An irregular migrant from the Continent to the south of England. A few records go as far north as Scotland but this is exceptional. It has probably bred at sites where individuals have been seen for a few years in succession. The population of visitors is mostly male. Its range extends from the Mediterranean to Scandinavia and eastwards to Kamchatka and Japan.

A late-summer migrant, most often seen in July and August, rarely in September.

eighth and ninth segments, and varying degrees of black along the sides. The upper claspers are pointed and the lower one triangular and curved upwards slightly. The wings always have an extensive area of saffron at the base, particularly on the deep hindwings. In some individuals the saffron extends along the costa. The veins are orange in the wing patches but black elsewhere. The pterostigma is yellow to red between two thick black lines.

Young males are similar in body colour to mature females, which have a yellow frons and ochre to brown eyes. The thorax and abdomen vary from straw to ochre yellow in females. The anal appendages are short and pointed. In the female the saffron tends to be more extensive on the wings.

Red-Veined Darter

Nearly mature male

Average length 40 mm.
Average wingspan 60 mm.

The largest red Darter to be found in Britain is unfortunately a rare visitor. The red veins and bluish tinge to the wings may not be immediately obvious but along with the distinctive anal claspers they are the best diagnostic features. The Vagrant Darter *Sympetrum vulgatum* sometimes has a reddish tinge to the wings but is so different in other ways that confusion is very unlikely at close quarters.

Description
The mature male has two-tone eyes of red above and blue below that are quite distinctive when

Male (note the blue and red eyes)

Nearly mature female

Nearly mature female

seen from the front. The frons is bright red with a black line across the vertex that extends down the side of the eyes. The top of the thorax is red but the sides are yellowish turning to grey-brown and marked by three thin black lines. The legs are black with some yellow or red on them. The abdomen is a bright scarlet red; in some lights the colour appears pinkish. The first segment and part of the second are black, and the eighth and ninth segments each have a black streak or spot along the top. In some males the black markings may be absent. The long red upper appendages are pointed and bowed inwards slightly. The lower triangular-shaped appendage curves upwards. The red colouring extends along most of the veins with age but is not immediately obvious when the dragonfly is in flight. There is a touch of saffron at the base of each wing and the pterostigma is yellow to red between two thick black lines.

Females and young males have similar markings to the mature male but the overall colour is yellow to ochre in place of red. In addition the female abdomen has a whitish bloom underneath and the wing veins may be more yellow than red in some individuals. The anal appendages are short and turned inwards slightly.

Larva Average length 18 mm.
The eggs hatch a few weeks after being laid and growth is completed in a year. The only *Sympetrum* species not to have dorsal spines (the laterals are short too) although the overall shape of the head and body is typical of the genus. It has longer antennae than *S. striolatum*. Weedy ponds and lakes are the preferred habitat.

Behaviour and Habitat
The male will sun itself on bare ground or vegetation between sorties out over the open water of a pond or lake. The flight is fast and zigzag between hovering pauses. The female remains in nearby vegetation and is mated soon after visiting the water margins. Copulation takes place on herbage and the male usually accompanies the female as she oviposits into open water.

Sheltered ponds and lakes with rushy margins in lowland areas are the most likely sites for this species.

Distribution and Time of Appearance
A powerful migrant that makes rare visits to southern England (even more rarely seen further north) from Europe and North Africa. It has probably bred in Britain a few times but needs a warmer winter to establish itself in a new area. The range of this species extends across southern Europe and North Africa to India and China. It also occurs in southern Africa.

It arrives in Britain in July and August, exceptionally a month either side.

Ruddy Darter

Mature male (note the waisted abdomen)

Mature male

Average length 34 mm.
Average wingspan 55 mm.

The Ruddy Darter *S. sanguineum* is a small red Darter easily confused with the slightly larger Common Darter *S. striolatum* with which it may share habitats. The red abdomen of the mature male is much brighter, more crimson than scarlet, and its mode of flight is more jerky than the common species.

Description

The distinctive features of the male are the red face and frons with a dark black line across the vertex extending down the edge of the eyes, which are deep red on top, dark green below. Note the black collar on the prothorax. The thorax is reddy brown, almost bronze coloured, with black lines delineating the segments. Both sexes have black legs except for red or yellow at the base. The third and fifth segments of the abdomen are constricted slightly, giving it a waisted look; along both sides of the segments from the third to the eighth there is a black line. The red coloration develops from the abdomen upwards after warmth and exposure to the sun.

The immature male is similar to the female, which has a lemon-yellow face, and eyes that are light brown on top and lemon on the sides. Females may develop some red coloration with age. There are black markings similar to the male's on the head, thorax and abdomen. The wing veins are black with only a touch of saffron at the wing-bases, which may extend along the costa in mature specimens.

Larva Average length 15–17 mm.
The eggs may diapause if laid late and the larva hatches in spring, growing rapidly after May to an

Sympetrum sanguineum (MULLER 1764)

Mature female

Mature female

unsynchronized emergence between July and September. It has a large five-sided head with big eyes and a broad abdomen with mid-dorsal spines on the fifth to eighth segments. Slightly shorter lateral spines – otherwise difficult to distinguish from *S. striolatum*. See the key for differences in the premental setae. It is a dark greeny brown colour and is found in ponds and lakes among the roots of horsetails and bulrushes.

Behaviour and Habitat

This species has a distinct preference for muddy pools that have plenty of lush vegetation, particularly where horsetails and rushes grow, on which the males like to sun themselves. If the breeding site is tidied up this brilliant red Darter no longer stays to breed. During the warmer part of the day the male will sit on an exposed perch along the water margin and make frequent sorties to catch food or attack intruding males. They hover more than *S. striolatum* and have a distinctive swinging flight. Females remain concealed in neighbouring vegetation to mate for several minutes before flying off in tandem to open water. The female may oviposit alone or be accompanied by the male as she dips up and down, sometimes dropping eggs into the water, at other times washing them free as the tip of the abdomen touches the surface.

Distribution and Time of Appearance

This species, already uncommon, is becoming rarer, possibly through loss of habitat. It is found in southern England and Wales as well as many localities in Eire. Sometimes the population is boosted by an influx of Continental immigrants. It has a widespread distribution in Europe from southern Scandinavia to Spain and Portugal.

On the wing between July and September.

Common Darter

Mature male

Average length 37 mm.
Average wingspan 58 mm.

This species is the most common and widespread of the red Darters. Almost any unpolluted pond in late summer will be encircled by a busy population of territorial males. An individual may be encouraged to perch nearer to the observer if something white is left in its territory and no sudden movements are made towards it.

The *Sympetrums* can be distinguished from the *Orthetrum* genus by the lack of shoulder stripes and from the *Libellulas* by the absence of dark patches at the wingbase. The Common Darter *S. striolatum* is slightly larger and of a less intense red than the Ruddy Darter *S. sanguineum*.

The Vagrant Darter *Sympetrum vulgatum* (Lin-naeus 1758) is so similar to the Common Darter *S. striolatum* that it can only be distinguished after close examination. It has a black line above the frons, which extends a fair way down the sides, and in the male a black line runs along the side of the first three abdominal segments. In the female the vulvar scale is thinner and protrudes at 90°. It is a migrant from the Continent recorded seven or eight times in all but has probably been overlooked because of its similarity to the Common Darter.

The Southern Darter *Sympetrum meridionale* (Selys 1841) has been recorded a couple of times as a vagrant. The distinguishing features of this species are the pale yellow sides to the thorax devoid of any black markings. The female has a blunt vulvar scale.

Sympetrum striolatum (CHARPENTIER 1840)

Mature male

Mature female

Mature female head (note the line between the eyes does not extend down the sides)

Description

The immature male has similar colouring to the female. In a mature male the eyes are red on top, yellow-brown below, and the frons is crimson. A narrow black line extends across the front of the vertex but does not go down the sides of the frons. The thorax is yellow-brown dorsally with red wing attachments. The sides are yellow broken by areas of red, sometimes forming a middle band. Narrow black lines mark out the thoracic divisions. The legs are dark brown with a yellow base and a thin yellow line along the outside. The abdomen is crimson with very small pairs of black and yellow spots on the third to eighth segments. The dark marks along the sides of these segments do not form a continuous line. The upper claspers are pointed and cylindrical, and are as long as the last two segments; the lower one is triangular and slightly curved upwards. The wings are clear with a touch of saffron at the wingbases. Old individuals may have a brownish tinge to the wings. The pterostigma varies from yellow to brown-red.

The female has a yellow-brown and ochre head, thorax and abdomen, marked black as in the male. Mature females may acquire varying degrees of red along the centre of the abdomen. The female appendages are short. The vulvar scale protrudes at an angle of 30°, and the tip is slightly notched, unlike the Vagrant Darter *S. vulgatum*.

Continental immigrants tend to be slightly larger, paler and less well marked.

Larva Average length 15–18 mm.

The large five-sided head bears quite big eyes as do the other *Sympetrums*. The broad abdomen has mid-dorsal spines on segments four to eight and long incurved spines along the sides of segments eight and nine. It is very similar to the Ruddy Darter *S. sanguineum* but can best be distinguished by the premental setae illustrated in the key. The eggs hatch after a few weeks but growth is slow until May when there follows a rapid growth spurt to an unsynchronized emergence in late summer. The mud and weeds of ponds, lakes and canals are the favoured habitat.

Behaviour and Habitat

Often seen sunbathing on a log or bare patch of ground, it seems to have a preference for light-coloured surfaces; it makes frequent darting sorties of several metres before returning to its original perch. The males are most often seen around midday defending a patch of territory on the margins of a pond or lake. Both sexes may also be found some distance from water, along hedgerows or in woodland clearings.

The female visits open water to mate and is usually seized on arrival by a male. If this does not occur immediately she will advertise her presence by flying up and down in a distinctive dipping flight. The pair perch on marginal vegetation to mate for several minutes before flying off in tandem to open water, where they bob up and down, as the female dips the tip of her abdomen into the water and the eggs are washed away.

Distribution and Time of Appearance

One of our commonest Darter dragonflies. It is found in virtually every county in England, Wales and Ireland, but is replaced by the Highland Darter *S. nigrescens* in Scotland. On the Continent its range extends northwards from the Mediterranean to southern Scandinavia, eastwards to Russia, and south-eastwards, finally, to Iran and Kashmir. It is represented in the Far East by two subspecies.

The flight period is from mid June to the end of October. Most often seen in August and September.

Mature male

Mature female

Highland Darter *Sympetrum nigrescens* (LUCAS 1911)

The distinction between the Highland Darter *S. nigrescens* and the Common Darter is still a matter of debate and many authorities would consider them to be two forms of the same species.

The most obvious distinction is that the Highland Darter is an altogether darker, almost charred version, of the common southern species. It breeds along the western Highlands of Scotland and in parts of Ireland and south Norway. Intermediate forms have been recorded in the north of England. It is most common in western maritime areas because of the milder winters experienced at such northern latitudes. Further eastwards the climate becomes too cold for it to breed. Certainly this species is not unusual as a darker more northerly form, which is better adapted to absorbing the available heat. Melanism is frequently seen under similar circumstances in other insects.

The larva, behaviour and habitat requirements are the same as the Common Darter *S. striolatum* and its flight period is only slightly curtailed by the colder climate.

Mature male

Mature female

Mature male

Mature female

White-Faced Darter

Mature male

Mature male (note the white face)

Average length 37 mm.
Average wingspan 53 mm.

The aptly named White-Faced Darter is a small black dragonfly marked with yellow or crimson according to age and sex. It is only likely to be confused with the Black Darter *Sympetrum danae* if the white frons is not visible. Territorial males patrol over small dark peat pools, daintily hovering one moment, then darting forth to engage in dogfights the next. They are very attractive, particularly when the sun catches the smoky blue tinge of their wings, but observers should sit quietly, as they will disappear at the least disturbance.

Unfortunately they have very specific habitat requirements which have restricted their range to the Highlands of Scotland and a few isolated colonies further south where sheltered sphagnum bog still survives.

Description

The frons and clypeus are a distinctive off-white above black mouthparts and the eyes are brown-black above, olive green below, becoming smoky black in old individuals. The black hairy thorax with black legs has shoulder stripes and two lateral bars which vary from dark orange to crimson in the male. The abdomen is likewise marked by crimson dorsal spots on an otherwise black background. The pointed upper appendages and the square lower one all curve upwards slightly. All four wings have small black bases and some white along the costa on either side of the dark brown pterostigmata.

Young males and mature females are very similar to the mature male except that the red is replaced by yellow. With ageing in females the yellow darkens to ochre and a blue pruinescence may develop along the sides of the abdomen. The female appendages are short and pointed.

Larva Average length 18–20 mm.
The *Sympetrum*-like larva can readily be distinguished by a characteristic mottled ventral surface to the abdomen. The head has an oval shape, seen from above, and a triangular spoon-shaped labium. The body is slightly flattened and triangular in section, with mid-dorsal spines on the fourth, fifth and sixth segments and lateral spines on the eighth and ninth, not particularly hairy.

Growth takes over two years usually ending in spring and early summer emergence. Sphagnum bogs and acidic peat pools are the favoured habitat.

Mature female

Newly emerged male above its larval exuvia

Behaviour and Habitat

The White-Faced Dragonfly is restricted to sphagnum bog pools for its breeding, preferably with some shelter from the wind. It is severely threatened by drainage and forestry plantations.

Each male patrols a territorial patch over an area of sphagnum bog, hovering and darting around. Individuals may fly parallel to one another at the boundary before parting. Aggression and territoriality increase through the season as the population density declines. A visiting female is soon grasped and the pair fly to nearby vegetation in the wheel position. After mating the unaccompanied female deposits her eggs in the watery patches of the sphagnum bog.

Distribution and Time of Appearance

A fairly wide distribution in the Highlands of Scotland where a suitable habitat occurs, but very rare elsewhere. There are isolated colonies in Cumbria, Cheshire, Derbyshire and Surrey. In Europe its boreo-alpine range takes in Scandinavia, and central and southern Europe as far as the Pyrenees and Alps.

It is an early dragonfly, on the wing from the end of May to the end of July, most common in June and July.

White face of male

Female Brown Hawker (*Aeshna grandis*)

GLOSSARY

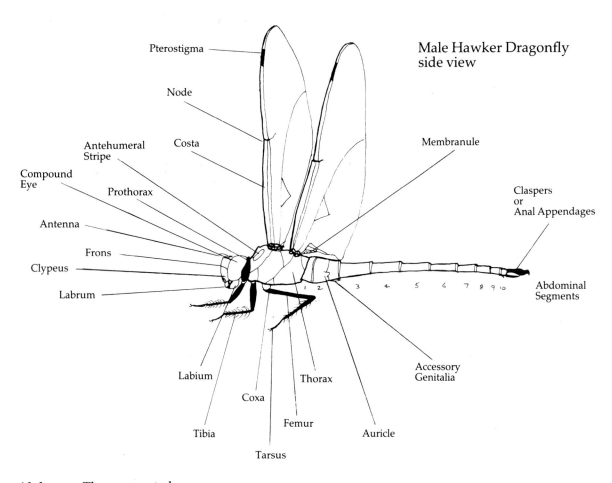

Pterostigma

Node

Costa

Antehumeral Stripe

Compound Eye

Prothorax

Antenna

Frons

Clypeus

Labrum

Male Hawker Dragonfly
side view

Membranule

Claspers
or
Anal Appendages

Abdominal
Segments

Accessory
Genitalia

Labium

Coxa

Thorax

Femur

Auricle

Tibia

Tarsus

Abdomen The segmented
tail-like section of the body.

Accessory genitalia Structures
for retaining sperms, on the
underside of the second and
third segments of the
abdomen in the male.

Anal appendages At the end of
the abdomen, used by the
male to grip the female's
prothorax during copulation;
also called claspers.

Platycnemis pennipes

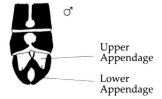

Upper
Appendage

Lower
Appendage

tip of damselfly abdomen
top view

Libellula quadrimaculata

tip of true dragonfly abdomen
top view

Andromorph A female form with the same colouring as the male.

Anisoptera A sub-order of Odonata referring to the true dragonflies which have, as the name implies, unequal-shaped forewings and hindwings.

Antehumeral stripes A pair of light-coloured stripes along the top of the thorax in some species.

Antennae The pair of sensory organs on the top of the head, feelers.

Auricles A pair of projections on the second abdominal segment of some anisopteran males. They guide the female's abdomen into the correct position during copulation.

Boreo-alpine Relating to northern and alpine habitats.

Caudal gills or lamellae The three leaf-like appendages of zygopteran larvae used for respiration and locomotion.

Cerci The outer pair of anal appendages on anisopteran larvae.

Claspers See anal appendages.

Clypeus The lowest part of the face of a dragonfly just above the labrum; in two parts, the anteclypeus and postclypeus.

Costa The major longitudinal vein running along the leading edge of each wing.

Coxa The segment at the base of the leg.

Diapause A resting period of no growth during the life cycle.

Distal Farthest from the centre of the body.

Dorsal Concerning the back or top side.

Ecdysis The moulting of the outer skin whereby the larva grows.

Encounter site The meeting place for the sexes, often a territory and an oviposition site.

Epiproct The middle anal appendage on anisopteran larvae.

Eutrophication The process whereby a stretch of water becomes increasingly enriched with nutrients and filled with vegetation.

Exuvia The cast of skin that remains after ecdysis.

Face The front area of the head consisting of the frons, clypeus and labrum.

Facet The surface of one of the ommatidia which collectively make up a compound eye.

Femur The third and often the largest segment of the leg counting from the foot.

Frons The front upper part of the head, anterior to the vertex and above the clypeus. The most prominent part of the face of anisopteran dragonflies.

Genitalia The sexual organs, beneath the second and third and the ninth segments in the male, and beneath the eighth and ninth segments in the female.

Genus A group of closely related species. The generic name is the first word in the scientific name, e.g. *Aeshna* is the genus for *Aeshna mixta*, *A. cyanea* and other species.

Gills The respiratory apparatus in larvae; most often the lining of the rectum in anisopteran larvae, and the caudal lamellae in zygopteran larvae.

Habitat The natural environment in which a dragonfly or its larva lives.

Imago The adult winged stage.

Immature See Teneral.

Instar The stage between two moults or ecdyses.

Labium The lower lip of a dragonfly's mouthparts; the mask *q.v.* of the larva.

Labrum The upper lip of the mouthparts.

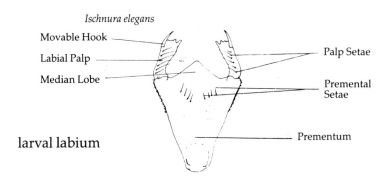

Ischnura elegans

Movable Hook

Labial Palp

Median Lobe

Palp Setae

Premental Setae

Prementum

larval labium

Lamellae See Caudal gills.
Larva The stage a young insect passes through before reaching the adult stage.

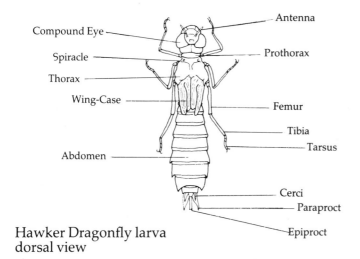

Hawker Dragonfly larva
dorsal view

Mandible The biting mouthparts.
Mask The modified labium of the larva used for catching prey. At rest the mask is held under the head but it can be projected rapidly forwards by hydraulic pressure.
Membranule An opaque triangular area near the base of the hindwing in Anisoptera.
Metamorphosis The changes that occur as a dragonfly develops from egg to larva to adult. Because there is no pupal stage, as in butterflies and other insects, the metamorphosis is said to be incomplete.

Neck See Prothorax.
Node A notch halfway along the leading edge of the wing.
Nose The frons and postclypeus together.

Ocelli A set of three simple eyes on top of the head in the vertex between the two large compound eyes.
Ommatidium A simple eye which is one of the many structural elements making up a compound eye.
Ovipositor The egg-laying structures on the eighth and ninth segments of some species of dragonfly, usually those that lay their eggs inside the stems of vegetation or in mud.

Hawker Dragonfly
♀ *Aeshna cyanea*

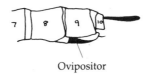

Ovipositor

tip of female abdomen
side view

Palps A pair of projections on the labium bearing bristles and hooks, used in the larva for gripping prey.
Paraprocts The inner pair of anal appendages on anisopteran larvae.
Prementum Central area of the labium in the larva.
Prolarva The first stage in metamorphosis immediately after hatching from the egg.
Prothorax The first segment of the thorax forming a neck between the head and body. Distinctive sculpting in the female corresponding to the shape of the male claspers is a useful guide to identification. Bears the first pair of legs.
Proximal Near the centre of the body.
Pruinescence A white or pale blue powdery coloration on the surface of a dragonfly's skin resembling the bloom on a plum.
Pterostigma A dark or coloured patch on the outer region of each wing, small and four-sided.

Rectum The final section of the gut; in anisopteran larvae it contains the brachial basket, a complex system of tracheal gills for respiration.
Rendezvous site See Encounter site.

Setae Hairs.
Species A group of individuals that can breed together to produce fertile offspring, the basic unit in classification. The specific name is the second word in the scientific name, e.g. *cyanea* is the

specific name of *Aeshna cyanea*.

Spiracle The opening to a trachea.

Tarsus The three segments and a claw that make up the foot on a dragonfly's leg.

Teneral The immature phase in an adult dragonfly's life between emergence and sexual maturity when the full colours are acquired.

Thorax The section of the body between the prothorax and abdomen. Strictly speaking the synthorax or pterothorax, composed of two fused segments bearing four wings and two pairs of legs.

Tibia The second section of the leg between the tarsus and the femur.

Tracheae Small tubes that carry air inside the dragonfly's body from paired openings called spiracles.

Ventral Concerning the underneath or lower surface of the body.

Vertex The area between the compound eyes on top of the head.

Vulvar scale All that remains of the anterior part of the ovipositor in those female Anisoptera that lay their eggs freely on the water.

Zygoptera A sub-order of Odonata referring to the damselflies, which have, as the scientific name implies, similar-shaped wings.

♀ Female
♂ Male

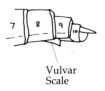

Darter Dragonfly
♀ *Sympetrum striolatum*

Vulvar Scale

tip of true dragonfly abdomen side view

Face of Brilliant Emerald (*Somatochlora metallica*)

KEY TO THE IDENTIFICATION OF ADULTS

Start here

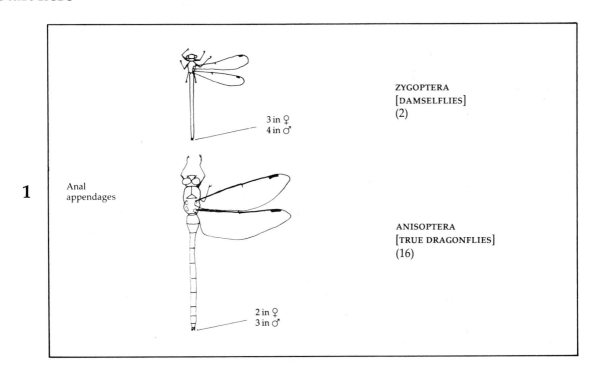

1	Anal appendages		ZYGOPTERA [DAMSELFLIES] (2)
		3 in ♀ 4 in ♂	
		2 in ♀ 3 in ♂	ANISOPTERA [TRUE DRAGONFLIES] (16)

ZYGOPTERA [DAMSELFLIES]

2	Metallic blue or green body	(3)
	Not so	(6)

3	♂ Wings coloured, body blue ♀ Wings tinted, body green Dense veins. Over 40 mm.	*Calopteryx* genus (4)
	♂ and ♀ Wings clear, body green Mature ♂ some blue Under 40 mm.	*Lestes* genus (5)

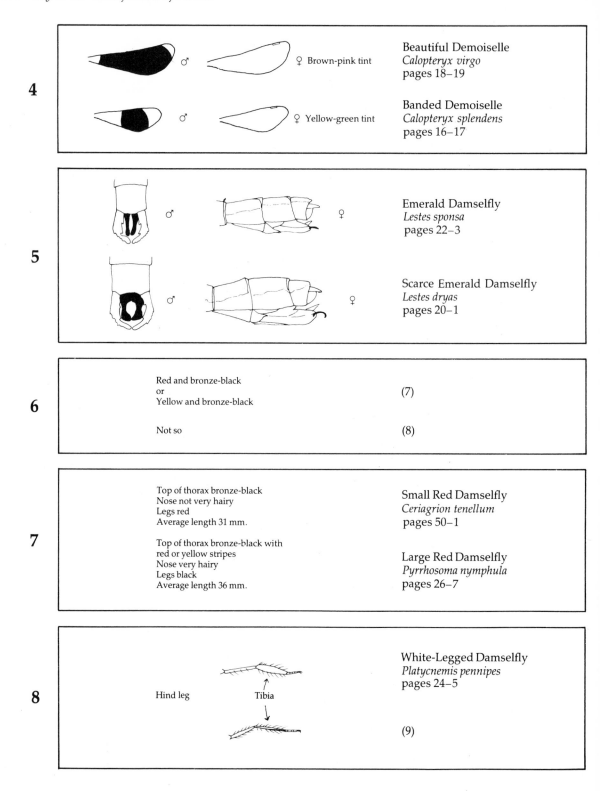

4

♂   ♀ Brown-pink tint

Beautiful Demoiselle
Calopteryx virgo
pages 18–19

♂   ♀ Yellow-green tint

Banded Demoiselle
Calopteryx splendens
pages 16–17

5

♂   ♀

Emerald Damselfly
Lestes sponsa
pages 22–3

♂   ♀

Scarce Emerald Damselfly
Lestes dryas
pages 20–1

6

Red and bronze-black
or
Yellow and bronze-black

(7)

Not so

(8)

7

Top of thorax bronze-black
Nose not very hairy
Legs red
Average length 31 mm.

Small Red Damselfly
Ceriagrion tenellum
pages 50–1

Top of thorax bronze-black with
red or yellow stripes
Nose very hairy
Legs black
Average length 36 mm.

Large Red Damselfly
Pyrrhosoma nymphula
pages 26–7

8

Hind leg   Tibia

White-Legged Damselfly
Platycnemis pennipes
pages 24–5

(9)

9

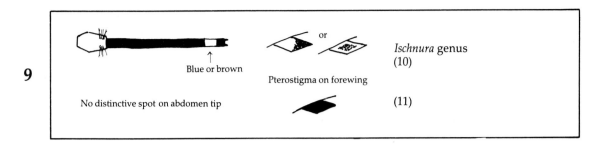

Blue or brown

No distinctive spot on abdomen tip

or

Pterostigma on forewing

Ischnura genus
(10)

(11)

10

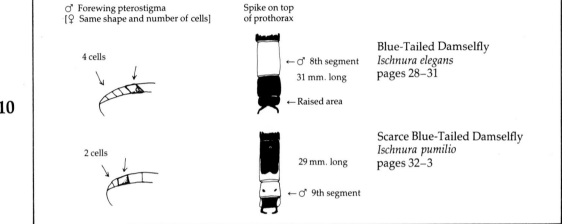

♂ Forewing pterostigma
[♀ Same shape and number of cells]

Spike on top
of prothorax

4 cells

2 cells

← ♂ 8th segment
31 mm. long

← Raised area

29 mm. long

← ♂ 9th segment

Blue-Tailed Damselfly
Ischnura elegans
pages 28–31

Scarce Blue-Tailed Damselfly
Ischnura pumilio
pages 32–3

11

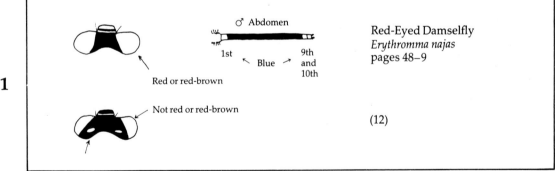

♂ Abdomen

1st   9th
← Blue →   and
              10th

Red or red-brown

Not red or red-brown

Red-Eyed Damselfly
Erythromma najas
pages 48–9

(12)

12

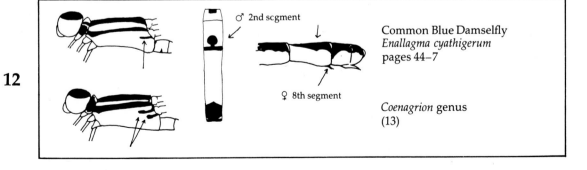

♂ 2nd segment

♀ 8th segment

Common Blue Damselfly
Enallagma cyathigerum
pages 44–7

Coenagrion genus
(13)

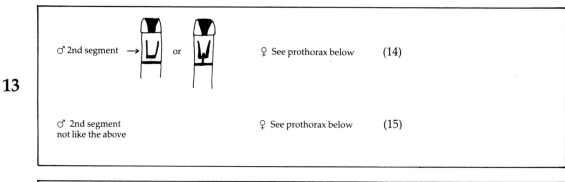

13

♂ 2nd segment → [or]   ♀ See prothorax below   (14)

♂ 2nd segment not like the above   ♀ See prothorax below   (15)

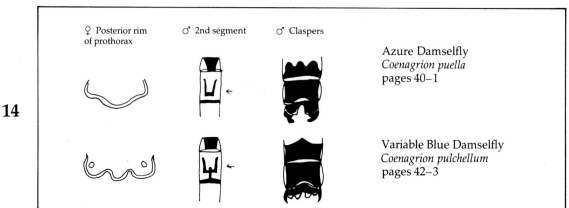

14

♀ Posterior rim of prothorax   ♂ 2nd segment   ♂ Claspers

Azure Damselfly
Coenagrion puella
pages 40–1

Variable Blue Damselfly
Coenagrion pulchellum
pages 42–3

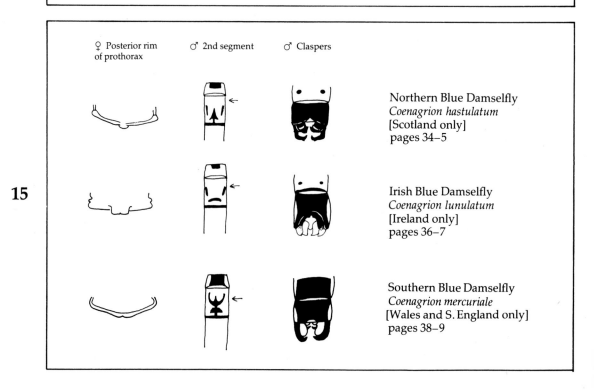

15

♀ Posterior rim of prothorax   ♂ 2nd segment   ♂ Claspers

Northern Blue Damselfly
Coenagrion hastulatum
[Scotland only]
pages 34–5

Irish Blue Damselfly
Coenagrion lunulatum
[Ireland only]
pages 36–7

Southern Blue Damselfly
Coenagrion mercuriale
[Wales and S. England only]
pages 38–9

ANISOPTERA [TRUE DRAGONFLIES]

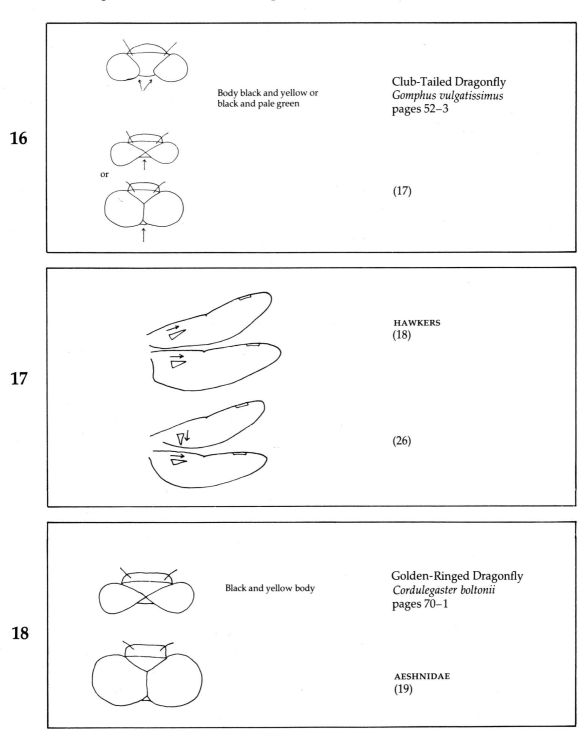

16

Body black and yellow or black and pale green

Club-Tailed Dragonfly
Gomphus vulgatissimus
pages 52–3

or

(17)

17

HAWKERS
(18)

(26)

18

Black and yellow body

Golden-Ringed Dragonfly
Cordulegaster boltonii
pages 70–1

AESHNIDAE
(19)

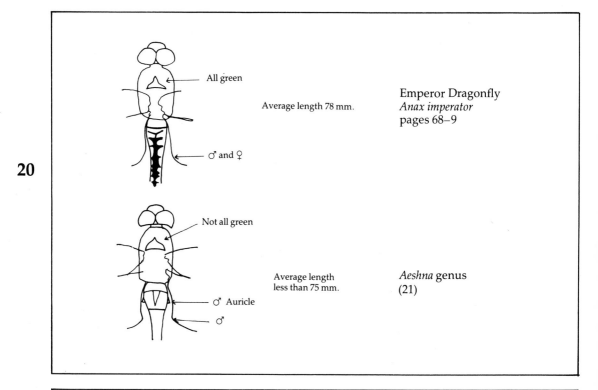

19

Hairy body

Pterostigma

Not so

Average length 55 mm.

♂

Average length over 60 mm.

♂

Hairy Dragonfly
Brachytron pratense
pages 54–5

(20)

20

All green

Average length 78 mm.

♂ and ♀

Not all green

Average length
less than 75 mm.

♂ Auricle

♂

Emperor Dragonfly
Anax imperator
pages 68–9

Aeshna genus
(21)

21

Brown body

Dark body with
blue, green or yellow spots

(22)

(23)

22

Blue or brown

♂ Blue spots

Brown Hawker
Aeshna grandis
pages 60–1

Green

Yellow

Norfolk Hawker
Aeshna isosceles
[East Anglia only]
pages 62–3

23

Over 70 mm.   (24)

Under 65 mm.   (25)

24

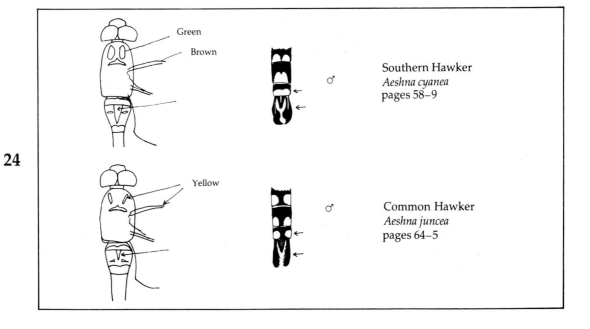

Green

Brown

♂

Southern Hawker
Aeshna cyanea
pages 58–9

Yellow

♂

Common Hawker
Aeshna juncea
pages 64–5

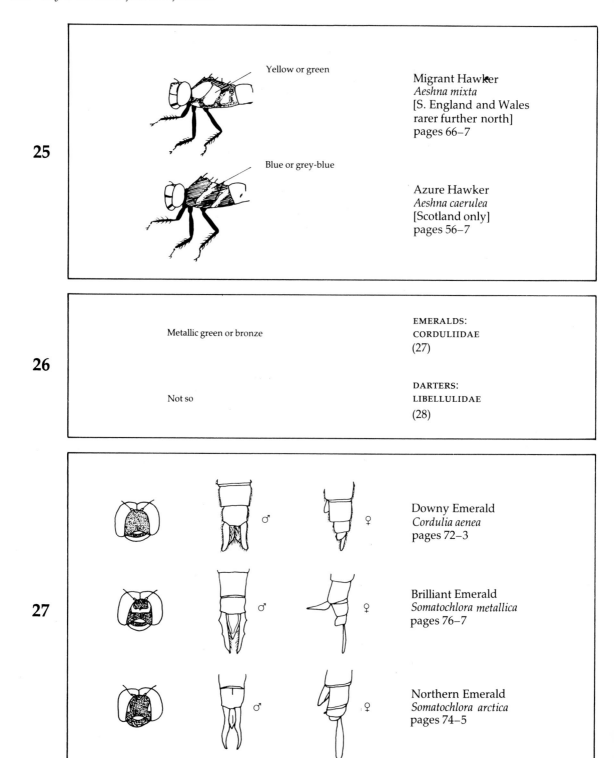

25

Yellow or green

Migrant Hawker
Aeshna mixta
[S. England and Wales
rarer further north]
pages 66–7

Blue or grey-blue

Azure Hawker
Aeshna caerulea
[Scotland only]
pages 56–7

26

Metallic green or bronze

**EMERALDS:
CORDULIIDAE**
(27)

Not so

**DARTERS:
LIBELLULIDAE**
(28)

27

♂   ♀

Downy Emerald
Cordulia aenea
pages 72–3

♂   ♀

Brilliant Emerald
Somatochlora metallica
pages 76–7

♂   ♀

Northern Emerald
Somatochlora arctica
pages 74–5

28

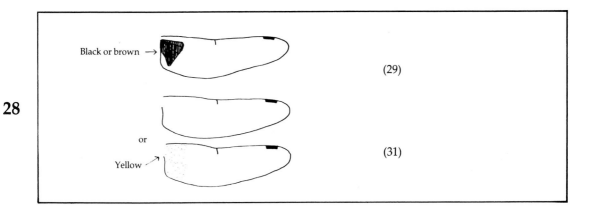

Black or brown → (29)

or
Yellow → (31)

29

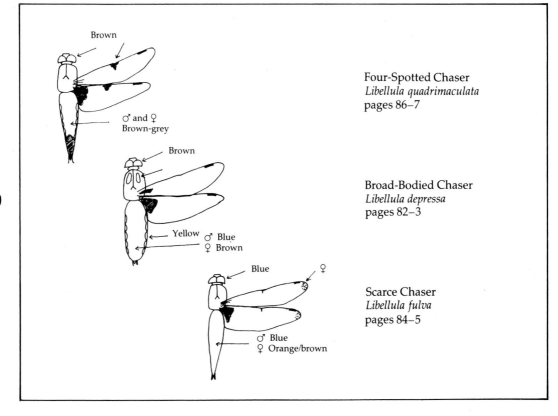

White-Faced Darter
Leucorrhinia dubia
pages 100–1

Libellula genus
(30)

30

Brown

♂ and ♀
Brown-grey

Four-Spotted Chaser
Libellula quadrimaculata
pages 86–7

Brown

Yellow   ♂ Blue
         ♀ Brown

Broad-Bodied Chaser
Libellula depressa
pages 82–3

Blue   ♀

♂ Blue
♀ Orange/brown

Scarce Chaser
Libellula fulva
pages 84–5

31

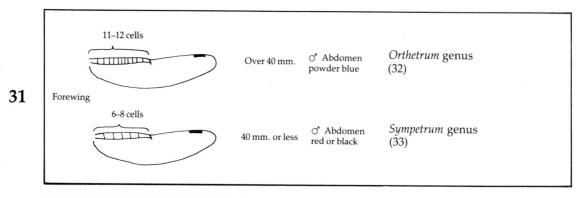

Forewing

11–12 cells

Over 40 mm.   ♂ Abdomen powder blue   *Orthetrum* genus (32)

6–8 cells

40 mm. or less   ♂ Abdomen red or black   *Sympetrum* genus (33)

32

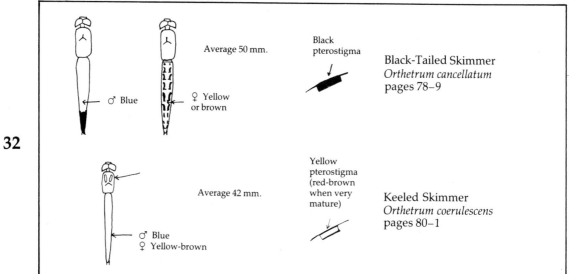

Average 50 mm.

♂ Blue   ♀ Yellow or brown

Black pterostigma

Black-Tailed Skimmer *Orthetrum cancellatum* pages 78–9

Average 42 mm.

♂ Blue
♀ Yellow-brown

Yellow pterostigma (red-brown when very mature)

Keeled Skimmer *Orthetrum coerulescens* pages 80–1

33

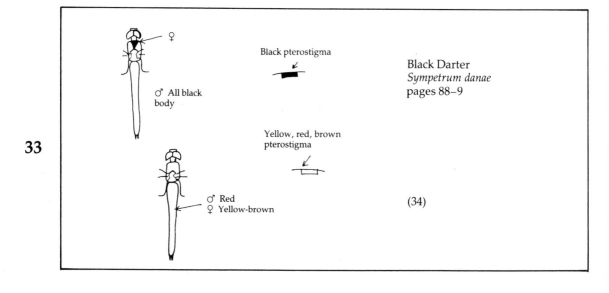

♀

♂ All black body

Black pterostigma

Black Darter *Sympetrum danae* pages 88–9

♂ Red
♀ Yellow-brown

Yellow, red, brown pterostigma

(34)

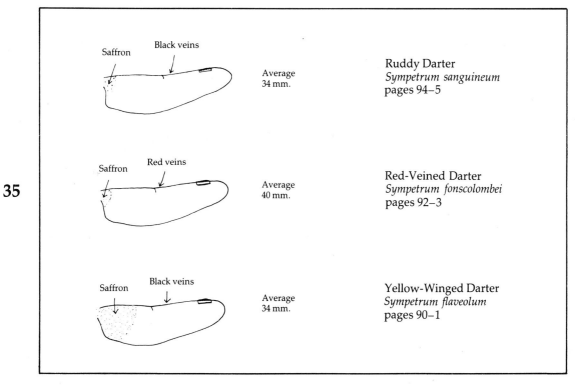

34

Common Darter
Sympetrum striolatum
or
Highland Darter
S. nigrescens
pages 96–9

(35)

35

Saffron   Black veins

Average
34 mm.

Ruddy Darter
Sympetrum sanguineum
pages 94–5

Saffron   Red veins

Average
40 mm.

Red-Veined Darter
Sympetrum fonscolombei
pages 92–3

Saffron   Black veins

Average
34 mm.

Yellow-Winged Darter
Sympetrum flaveolum
pages 90–1

KEY TO THE IDENTIFICATION OF LARVAE

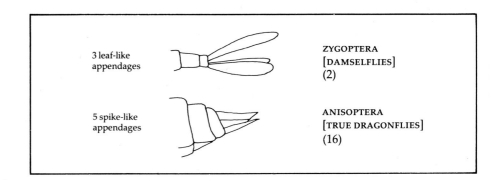

1   Tip of abdomen

3 leaf-like appendages → **ZYGOPTERA [DAMSELFLIES]** (2)

5 spike-like appendages → **ANISOPTERA [TRUE DRAGONFLIES]** (16)

ZYGOPTERA [DAMSELFLIES]

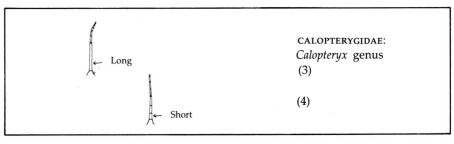

2   First segment of antenna

Long → **CALOPTERYGIDAE:** *Calopteryx* genus (3)

Short → (4)

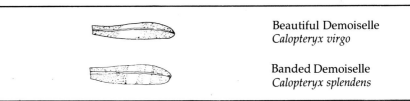

3   Caudal lamella

Beautiful Demoiselle *Calopteryx virgo*

Banded Demoiselle *Calopteryx splendens*

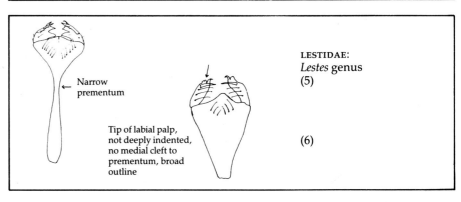

4

Narrow prementum → **LESTIDAE:** *Lestes* genus (5)

Tip of labial palp, not deeply indented, no medial cleft to prementum, broad outline → (6)

5   Hook of labial palp

3 setae   Scarce Emerald
Lestes dryas

2 setae   Emerald Damselfly
Lestes sponsa

6   Shape of tip of caudal lamella

PLATYCNEMIDIDAE:
Platycnemis genus
one species:
White-Legged Damselfly
Platycnemis pennipes

COENAGRIONIDAE
(7)

or rounded

7   Antenna

6 segments   (8)

7 segments   (10)

8   Caudal lamella

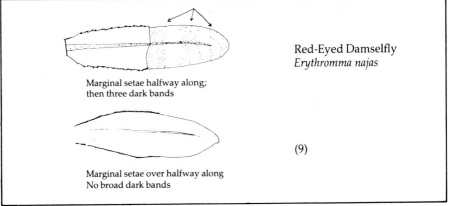

Marginal setae halfway along;
then three dark bands

Red-Eyed Damselfly
Erythromma najas

Marginal setae over halfway along
No broad dark bands

(9)

9   Caudal lamella

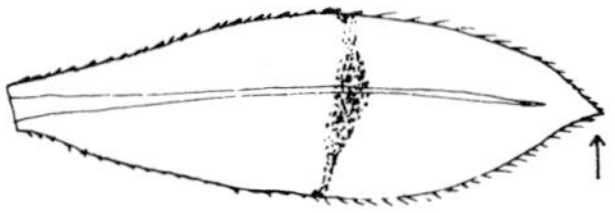

Slightly pointed tip
No prominent spotting on the head

Common Blue Damselfly
Enallagma cyathigerum

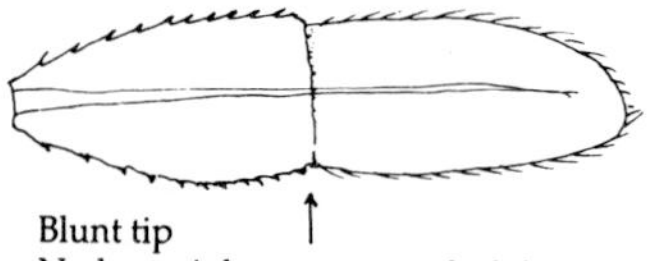

Blunt tip
Node straight across, no dark bands
Prominent spotting on the head

Northern Blue Damselfly
Coenagrion hastulatum
[recorded in Scotland]
or
Irish Blue Damselfly
Coenagrion lunulatum
[recorded in Ireland]

10   Caudal lamella

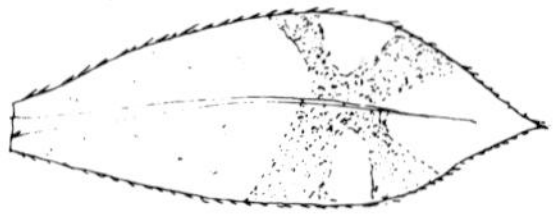

No node
Distinctive X pattern

Large Red Damselfly
Pyrrhosoma nymphula

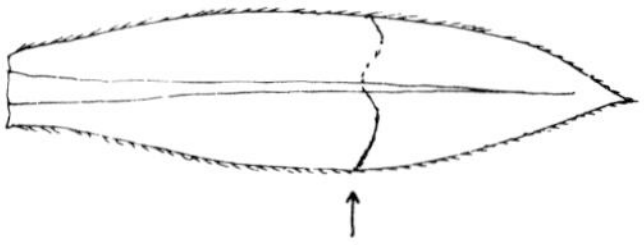

Nodal line present

(11)

11   Angle of node

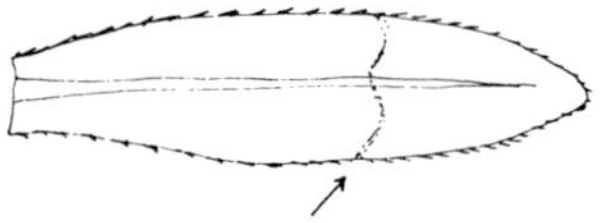

Node at right angles

(12)

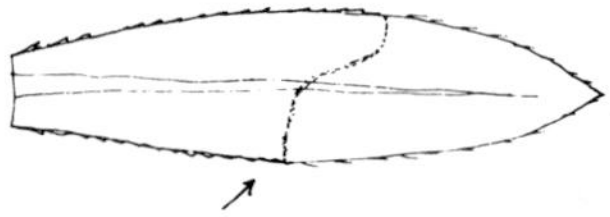

Node diagonal

(14)

12   Tip of caudal lamella

Pointed tip and many long setae
2 pale spots on head not
prominent

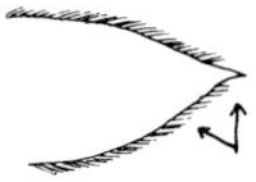

Southern Blue Damselfly
Coenagrion mercuriale

Blunt tip usually (if pointed,
sparse setae are distinguishing mark)
Prominent spots on head

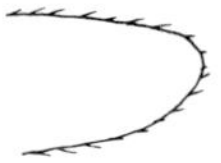

(13)

13

Larva usually green with brown wing-sheaths and lamellae	**Azure Damselfly** *Coenagrion puella*
Larva usually brown to sepia (rarely green)	**Variable Blue Damselfly** *Coenagrion pulchellum*

14 Postnodal edge of lamella

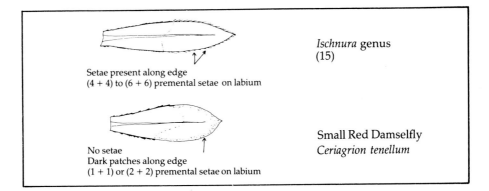

Setae present along edge
(4 + 4) to (6 + 6) premental setae on labium — *Ischnura* genus (15)

No setae
Dark patches along edge
(1 + 1) or (2 + 2) premental setae on labium — **Small Red Damselfly** *Ceriagrion tenellum*

15 Labial setae

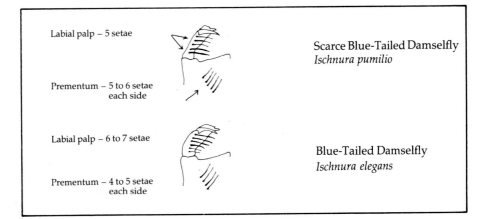

Labial palp – 5 setae

Prementum – 5 to 6 setae each side — **Scarce Blue-Tailed Damselfly** *Ischnura pumilio*

Labial palp – 6 to 7 setae

Prementum – 4 to 5 setae each side — **Blue-Tailed Damselfly** *Ischnura elegans*

ANISOPTERA [TRUE DRAGONFLIES]

16 Antenna

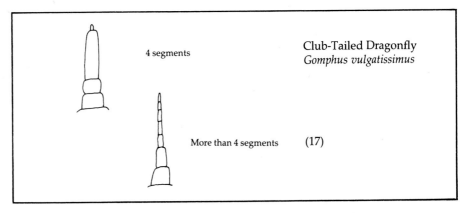

4 segments — **Club-Tailed Dragonfly** *Gomphus vulgatissimus*

More than 4 segments — (17)

17 Labium from the front

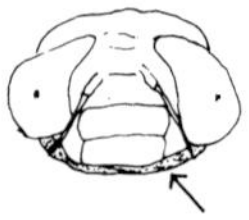

Clypeus and labrum visible — **AESHNIDAE** (18)

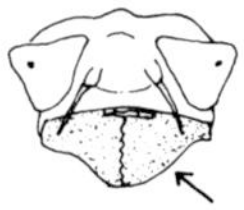

Covers clypeus and labrum — (24)

18 Eye shape

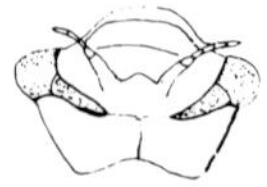

Small eyes — **Hairy Dragonfly** *Brachytron pratense*

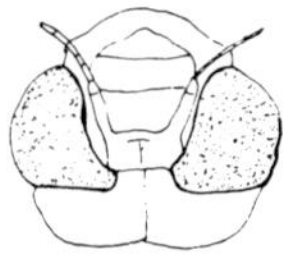

Large eyes, straight posterior edge — **Emperor Dragonfly** *Anax imperator*

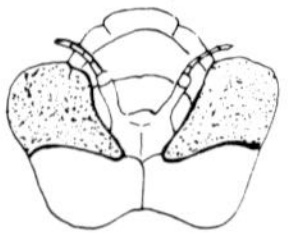

Large eyes, posterior edge not straight — *Aeshna* genus (19)

19

Under 38 mm. — (20)

Over 38 mm. — (21)

20 Lateral spines on segment 9

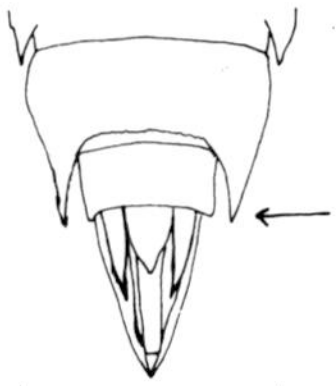

Spines as long as segment 10 [south of Scotland] — **Migrant Hawker** *Aeshna mixta*

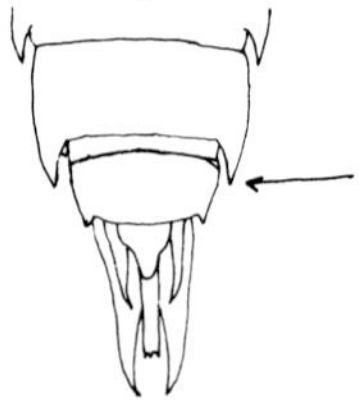

Spines not as long as segment 10 [Scotland only] — **Azure Hawker** *Aeshna caerulea*

21 Anal appendages

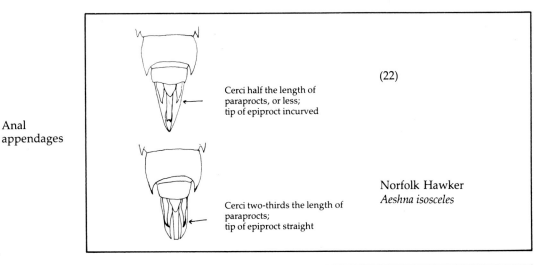

Cerci half the length of paraprocts, or less; tip of epiproct incurved

(22)

Cerci two-thirds the length of paraprocts; tip of epiproct straight

Norfolk Hawker
Aeshna isosceles

22 Shape of labium

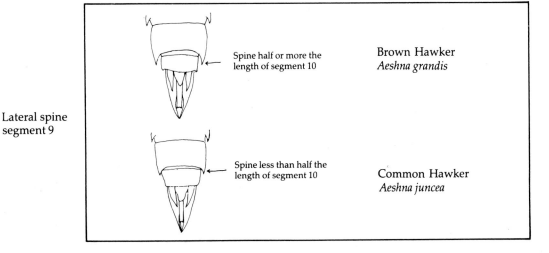

Narrow

Southern Hawker
Aeshna cyanea

Broad

(23)

23 Lateral spine segment 9

Spine half or more the length of segment 10

Brown Hawker
Aeshna grandis

Spine less than half the length of segment 10

Common Hawker
Aeshna juncea

24   Labial palp

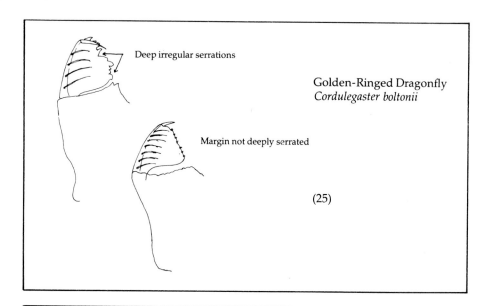

Deep irregular serrations

Golden-Ringed Dragonfly
Cordulegaster boltonii

Margin not deeply serrated

(25)

25   Anal appendages

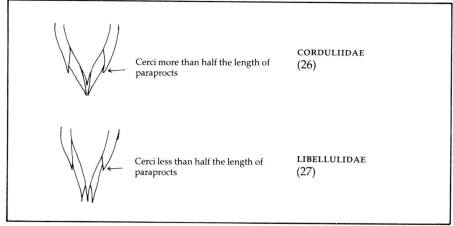

Cerci more than half the length of paraprocts

CORDULIIDAE
(26)

Cerci less than half the length of paraprocts

LIBELLULIDAE
(27)

26   Dorsal spines

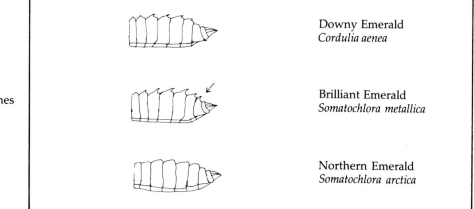

Downy Emerald
Cordulia aenea

Brilliant Emerald
Somatochlora metallica

Northern Emerald
Somatochlora arctica

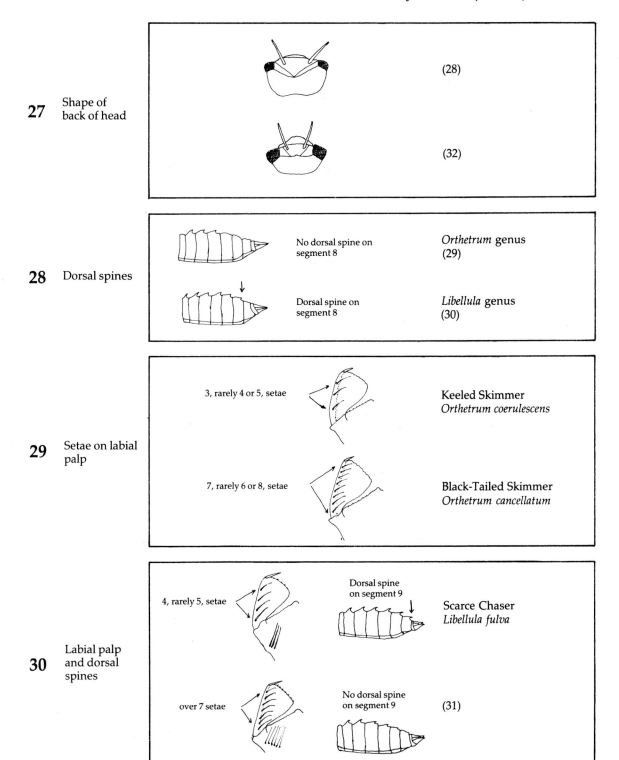

27 Shape of back of head — (28) / (32)

28 Dorsal spines
- No dorsal spine on segment 8 — *Orthetrum* genus (29)
- Dorsal spine on segment 8 — *Libellula* genus (30)

29 Setae on labial palp
- 3, rarely 4 or 5, setae — Keeled Skimmer *Orthetrum coerulescens*
- 7, rarely 6 or 8, setae — Black-Tailed Skimmer *Orthetrum cancellatum*

30 Labial palp and dorsal spines
- 4, rarely 5, setae — Dorsal spine on segment 9 — Scarce Chaser *Libellula fulva*
- over 7 setae — No dorsal spine on segment 9 — (31)

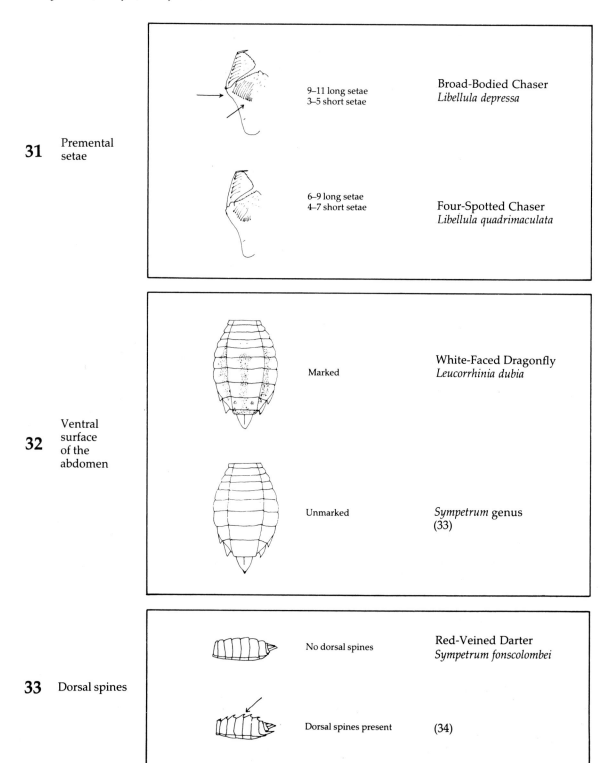

31   Premental setae

9–11 long setae
3–5 short setae

Broad-Bodied Chaser
Libellula depressa

6–9 long setae
4–7 short setae

Four-Spotted Chaser
Libellula quadrimaculata

32   Ventral surface of the abdomen

Marked

White-Faced Dragonfly
Leucorrhinia dubia

Unmarked

Sympetrum genus
(33)

33   Dorsal spines

No dorsal spines

Red-Veined Darter
Sympetrum fonscolombei

Dorsal spines present

(34)

34   Lateral spine on segment 9

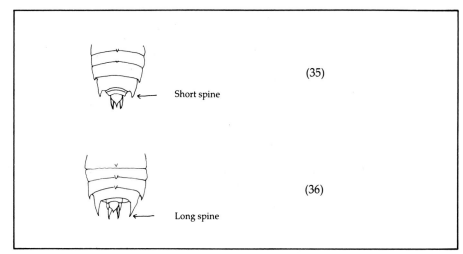

Short spine — (35)

Long spine — (36)

35   Labial palp setae

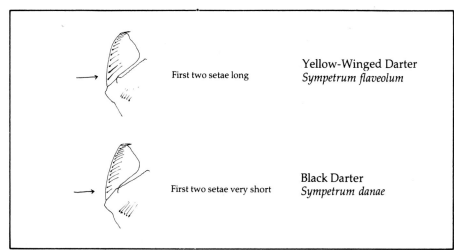

First two setae long — **Yellow-Winged Darter** *Sympetrum flaveolum*

First two setae very short — **Black Darter** *Sympetrum danae*

36   Premental setae

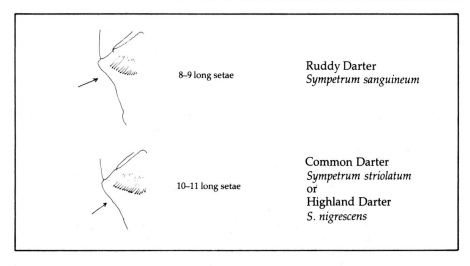

8–9 long setae — **Ruddy Darter** *Sympetrum sanguineum*

10–11 long setae — **Common Darter** *Sympetrum striolatum* or **Highland Darter** *S. nigrescens*

FURTHER READING

Aguilar, J. d', Dommanget, J.-L., and Préchac, R., *Guide des libellules d'Europe et d'Afrique du Nord*, Delachaux et Niestlé, Neuchâtel and Paris, 1985.

Corbet, P. S., *A Biology of Dragonflies*, 2nd edition, E. W. Classey, Faringdon, Oxon, 1984.

Corbet, P. S., Longfield, C. and Moore, N. W., *Dragonflies*, 2nd edition, New Naturalist series, Collins, London, 1985.

Fraser, F. C., *Odonata: Handbook for the Identification of British Insects*, I (10), Royal Entomological Society, London, 1956.

Hammond, C. O., *The Dragonflies of Great Britain & Ireland*, 2nd edition, revd by Merritt, R., Harley Books, Colchester, Essex, 1983.

King, A. and Clifford, S., *Holding Your Ground, An action guide to local conservation*, Maurice Temple Smith, London, 1985.

Longfield, C., *The Dragonflies of the British Isles*, Warne, London, 1949.

Lucas, W. J., *British Dragonflies (Odonata)*, Upcott Gill, London, 1900.

Mabey, R., *The Pollution Handbook*, Penguin Education, Harmondsworth, 1974.

Journal of the British Dragonfly Society – twice yearly to members of the British Dragonfly Society, contact address: page 12.

Odonatologica, a quarterly, *Notulae Odonatologicae*, a semi-annual bulletin, and *Selysia*, a semi-annual newsletter to members of the Societas Internationalis Odonatologica (S.I.O.), U.K. contact: Dr P. J. Mill, Department of Pure and Applied Zoology, University of Leeds, LS2 9JT.

CHECK LIST

There follows a complete list of Odonata recorded in the British Isles. They are grouped according to sub-order and family, and listed by the full scientific name (made up of the generic name, the specific name, the name of the first person to describe the species, and the year in which the description was published), followed by the vernacular name and page reference. In the section on British Dragonflies, to which the page numbers refer, each of the breeding species is presented in a similar way: an account of the main distinguishing features; a detailed description of the male and of any differences which distinguish the female; the key features of the larva, including its preferred habitat; the behaviour and habitat of the species; and the distribution and time of appearance of the species. Extinct and accidental species are marked as follows in the check list:

× means the species is extinct in the British Isles;
* means a migrant or vagrant that has not become a regular and established breeding species;
† means a species that has been recorded in the Channel Isles but not in Great Britain or Ireland.

The extinct and accidental species are given reference in the introductory paragraphs dealing with a related species, and the relevant page number in the check list is given in parentheses.

Order   ODONATA

Sub-Order ZYGOPTERA

Family Calopterygidae
Calopteryx (Leach 1815)
    splendens (Harris 1782)   Banded Demoiselle 16–17
    virgo (Linnaeus 1758)   Beautiful Demoiselle 18–19

Family Lestidae
Sympecma (Burmeister 1839)
†   *fusca* (van der Linden 1820)   Brown Emerald Damselfly (20)
Lestes (Leach 1815)
†   *barbarus* (Fabricius 1798)   Shy Emerald Damselfly (20)
    dryas (Kirby 1890)   Scarce Emerald Damselfly 20–1
    sponsa (Hansemann 1823)   Emerald Damselfly 22–3
*†   *viridis* (van der Linden 1825)   Green Emerald Damselfly (20)

Family Platycnemididae
Platycnemis (Burmeister 1839)
    pennipes (Pallas 1771)   White-Legged Damselfly 24–5

Family Coenagrionidae
  Pyrrhosoma (Charpentier 1840)
    nymphula (Sulzer 1776)   Large Red Damselfly 26–7
  Ischnura (Charpentier 1840)
    elegans (van der Linden 1823)   Blue-Tailed Damselfly 28–31
    pumilio (Charpentier 1825)   Scarce Blue-Tailed Damselfly 32–3
  Coenagrion (Kirby 1890)
×   *armatum* (Charpentier 1840)   Norfolk Blue Damselfly (36)
    hastulatum (Charpentier 1825)   Northern Blue Damselfly 34–5
    lunulatum (Charpentier 1840)   Irish Blue Damselfly 36–7
    mercuriale (Charpentier 1840)   Southern Blue Damselfly 38–9
    puella (Linnaeus 1758)   Azure Damselfly 40–1
    pulchellum (van der Linden 1825)   Variable Blue Damselfly 42–3
×   *scitulum* (Rambur 1842)   Dainty Blue Damselfly (38)
  Enallagma (Charpentier 1840)
    cyathigerum (Charpentier 1840)   Common Blue Damselfly 44–7
  Erythromma (Charpentier 1840)
    najas (Hansemann 1823)   Red-Eyed Damselfly 48–9
  Ceriagrion (Selys 1876)
    tenellum (de Villiers 1789)   Small Red Damselfly 50–1

Sub-Order ANISOPTERA

Family Gomphidae
  Gomphus (Leach 1815)
*   *flavipes* (Charpentier 1825)   Yellow-Legged Dragonfly (52)
    vulgatissimus (Linnaeus 1758)   Club-Tailed Dragonfly 52–3

Family Aeshnidae
  Brachytron (Selys 1850)
    pratense (Muller 1764)   Hairy Dragonfly 54–5
  Aeshna (Fabricius 1775)
*   *affinis* (van der Linden 1820)   Southern Migrant Hawker (66)
    caerulea (Strom 1783)   Azure Hawker 56–7
    cyanea (Muller 1764)   Southern Hawker 58–9
    grandis (Linnaeus 1758)   Brown Hawker 60–1
    isosceles (Muller 1767)   Norfolk Hawker 62–3
    juncea (Linnaeus 1758)   Common Hawker 64–5
    mixta (Latrielle 1805)   Migrant Hawker 66–7
  Anax (Leach 1815)
    imperator (Leach 1815)   Emperor Dragonfly 68–9
  Hemianax (Selys 1883)
*   *ephippiger* (Burmeister 1839)   Saddle-Back Dragonfly (68)

Family Corduligasteridae
  Cordulegaster (Leach 1815)
    boltonii (Donovan 1807)   Golden-Ringed Dragonfly 70–1

Family Corduliidae
    Cordulia (Leach 1815)
        aenea (Linnaeus 1758)   Downy Emerald 72–3
    Somatochlora (Selys 1871)
        alpestris (Selys 1840)   Alpine Emerald (74)
        arctica (Zetterstedt 1840)   Northern Emerald 74–5
        metallica (van der Linden 1825)   Brilliant Emerald 76–7
    Oxygastra (Selys 1870)
×   *curtisii* (Dale 1834)   Orange-Spotted Emerald (72)

Family Libellulidae
    Orthetrum (Newman 1833)
        cancellatum (Linnaeus 1758)   Black-Tailed Skimmer 78–9
        coerulescens (Fabricius 1798)   Keeled Skimmer 80–1
    Crocothemis (Brauer 1868)
†   *erythraea* (Brulle 1832)   Scarlet Dragonfly (80)
    Libellula (Linnaeus 1758)
        depressa (Linnaeus 1758)   Broad-Bodied Chaser 82–3
        fulva (Muller 1764)   Scarce Chaser 84–5
        quadrimaculata (Linnaeus 1758)   Four-Spotted Chaser 86–7
    Sympetrum (Newman 1833)
        danae (Sulzer 1776)   Black Darter 88–9
*   *flaveolum* (Linnaeus 1758)   Yellow-Winged Darter 90–1
*   *fonscolombei* (Selys 1840)   Red-Veined Darter 92–3
*   *meridionale* (Selys 1841)   Southern Darter (96)
        nigrescens (Lucas 1911)   Highland Darter 99
        sanguineum (Muller 1764)   Ruddy Darter 94–5
        striolatum (Charpentier 1840)   Common Darter 96–8
*   *vulgatum* (Linnaeus 1758)   Vagrant Darter (96)
    Leucorrhinia (Brittinger 1850)
        dubia (van der Linden 1825)   White-Faced Darter 100–1
    Pantala (Hagen 1861)
*   *flavescens* (Fabricius 1798)   Globe Skimmer (86)

INDEX

English Names

Alpine Emerald, 74
Azure Damselfly, 40–1
Azure Hawker, 56–7

Banded Demoiselle, 16–17
Beautiful Demoiselle, 18–19
Black Darter, 88–9
Black-Tailed Skimmer, 78–9
Blue-Tailed Damselfly, 28–31
Brilliant Emerald, 76–7
Broad-Bodied Chaser, 82–3
Brown Emerald Damselfly, 20
Brown Hawker, 60–1

Club-Tailed Dragonfly, 52–3
Common Blue Damselfly, 44–7
Common Darter, 96–8
Common Hawker, 64–5

Dainty Blue Damselfly, 38
Downy Emerald, 72–3

Emerald Damselfly, 22–3
Emperor Dragonfly, 68–9

Four-Spotted Chaser, 86–7

Globe Skimmer, 86
Golden-Ringed Dragonfly, 70–1
Green Emerald Damselfly, 20

Hairy Dragonfly, 54–5
Highland Darter, 99

Irish Blue Damselfly, 36–7

Keeled Skimmer, 80–1

Large Red Damselfly, 26–7

Migrant Hawker, 66–7

Norfolk Blue Damselfly, 36

Norfolk Hawker, 62–3
Northern Blue Damselfly, 34–5
Northern Emerald, 74–5

Orange-Spotted Emerald, 72

Red-Eyed Damselfly, 48–9
Red-Veined Darter, 92–3
Ruddy Darter, 94–5

Saddle-Back Dragonfly, 68
Scarce Blue-Tailed Damselfly, 32–3
Scarce Chaser, 84–5
Scarce Emerald Damselfly, 20–1
Scarlet Dragonfly, 80
Shy Emerald Damselfly, 20
Small Red Damselfly, 50–1
Southern Blue Damselfly, 38–9
Southern Darter, 96
Southern Hawker, 58–9
Southern Migrant Hawker, 66
Sub-Arctic Hawker, 65

Vagrant Darter, 96
Variable Blue Damselfly, 42–3

White-Faced Darter, 100–1
White-Legged Damselfly, 24–5

Yellow-Legged Dragonfly, 52
Yellow-Winged Darter, 90–1

Scientific Names

Forms (f) are listed under the full
  scientific name only.

aenea, Cordulia, 72–3
Aeshna affinis, 66
—caerulea, 56–7
—cyanea, 58–9
—grandis, 60–1

—isosceles, 62–3
—juncea, 64–5
—mixta, 66–7
—subarctica, 65
affinis, Aeshna, 66
alpestris, Somatochlora, 74
Anax imperator, 68–9
arctica, Somatochlora, 74–5
armatum, Coenagrion, 36

barbarus, Lestes, 20
boltonii, Cordulegaster, 70–1
Brachytron pratense, 54–5

caerulea, Aeshna, 56–7
Calopteryx splendens, 16–17
—virgo, 18–19
cancellatum, Orthetrum, 78–9
Ceriagrion tenellum, 50–1
—tenellum f. erythrogastrum, 50
—tenellum f. melanogastrum, 50
Coenagrion armatum, 36
—hastulatum, 34–5
—lunulatum, 36–7
—mercuriale, 38–9
—puella, 40–1
—puella f. annulatum, 40
—pulchellum, 42–3
—pulchellum f. nigrescens, 43
—scitulum, 38
coerulescens, Orthetrum, 80–1
Cordulegaster boltonii, 70–1
Cordulia aenea, 72–3
Crocothemis erythraea, 80
curtisii, Oxygastra, 72
cyanea, Aeshna, 58–9
cyathigerum, Enallagma, 44–7

danae, Sympetrum, 88–9
depressa, Libellula, 82–3
dryas, Lestes, 20–1
dubia, Leucorrhinia, 100–1

elegans, Ischnura, 28–31
Enallagma cyathigerum, 44–7
ephippiger, Hemianax, 68

erythraea, Crocothemis, 80
Erythromma najas, 48–9

flaveolum, Sympetrum, 90–1
flavescens, Pantala, 86
flavipes, Gomphus, 52
fonscolombei, Sympetrum, 92–3
fulva, Libellula, 84–5
fusca, Sympecma, 20

Gomphus flavipes, 52
—*vulgatissimus*, 52–3
grandis, Aeshna, 60–1

hastulatum, Coenagrion, 34–5
Hemianax ephippiger, 68

imperator, Anax, 68–9
Ischnura elegans, 28–31
—*elegans* f. *infuscans*, 31
—*elegans* f. *infuscans-obsoleta*, 31
—*elegans* f. *rufuscens*, 31
—*elegans* f. *violacea*, 31
Ischnura pumilio, 32–3
—*pumilio* f. *aurantiaca*, 33
isosceles, Aeshna, 62–3

juncea, Aeshna, 64–5

Lestes barbarus, 20
—*dryas*, 20–1

—*sponsa*, 22–3
—*viridis*, 20
Leucorrhinia dubia, 100–1
Libellula depressa, 82–3
—*fulva*, 84–5
—*quadrimaculata*, 86–7
—*quadrimaculata* f. *praenubila*, 87
lunulatum, Coenagrion, 36–7

mercuriale, Coenagrion, 38–9
meridionale, Sympetrum, 96
metallica, Somatochlora, 76–7
mixta, Aeshna, 66–7

najas, Erythromma, 48–9
nigrescens, Sympetrum, 99
nymphula, Pyrrhosoma, 26–7

Orthetrum cancellatum, 78–9
—*coerulescens*, 80–1
Oxygastra curtisii, 72

Pantala flavescens, 86
pennipes, Platycnemis, 24–5
Platycnemis pennipes, 24–5
—*pennipes* f. *lactea*, 24
pratense, Brachytron, 54–5
puella, Coenagrion, 40–1
pulchellum, Coenagrion, 42–3
pumilio, Ischnura, 32–3
Pyrrhosoma nymphula, 26–7

—*nymphula* f. *fulvipes*, 26
—*nymphula* f. *melanotum*, 26

quadrimaculata, Libellula, 86–7

sanguineum, Sympetrum, 94–5
scitulum, Coenagrion, 38
Somatochlora alpestris, 74
—*arctica*, 74–5
—*metallica*, 76–7
splendens, Calopteryx, 16–17
sponsa, Lestes, 22–3
striolatum, Sympetrum, 96–8
subarctica, Aeshna, 65
Sympecma fusca, 20
Sympetrum danae, 88–9
—*flaveolum*, 90–1
—*fonscolombei*, 92–3
—*meridionale*, 96
—*nigrescens*, 99
—*sanguineum*, 94–5
—*striolatum*, 96–8
—*vulgatum*, 96

tenellum, Ceriagrion, 50–1

virgo, Calopteryx, 18–19
viridis, Lestes, 20
vulgatissimus, Gomphus, 52–3
vulgatum, Sympetrum, 96